The Collector's
Handbook of
Lilliput Lane Cottages

The Collector's Handbook of Lilliput Lane Cottages

Annette Power

EMS AND ENS LTD

First published December 1994

© Text:
Annette Power 1994

© Photographs:
Stuart and Janette Allatt, Donna Morgan,
Annette Power, Stan Worrey 1994

ISBN 1-874558-02-7

Published by
Ems and Ens Ltd, Stapleton House, Langtree,
Torrington, Devon EX38 8NP

Printed in Great Britain by
Chichester Press Ltd, Chichester,
West Sussex PO19 2UW

Acknowledgements

I would like to offer my thanks to the many Lilliput Lane enthusiasts – both collectors and dealers – for their advice, help and support regarding the content of this book; my thanks also to Lilliput Lane Limited for an interesting tour of the Collectors Centre at Skirsgill, particularly the production process, which formed the basis for the section entitled 'Discovering Lilliput Lane Cottages'.

Special thanks must go to Stuart and Janette Allatt, Bob Douglas, Louise Irvine, Kevin Pearson and Stan Worrey for their assistance with the photographs and for their suggestions on the draft.

To everyone, thank you for making this book on the Lilliput Lane models possible.

Dedicated to my family –
especially my mother and my father –
for their encouragement and support
over the past eighteen months

Contents

Introduction

Towards the end of 1985 I purchased my first Lilliput Lane cottage; it was Tuck Shop from the English Collection – Northern and it took pride of place in my display cabinet at home. I was fascinated by the detail and accuracy of the model and by the attractive colouring. Little did I realise when I made this purchase that I had just been bitten by the collecting bug, and after Tuck Shop, Castle Street soon followed, and then Scroll on the Wall, and then . . .

And so it continued; the collection grew and grew. I considered limiting it to buildings from one particular region, however that approach failed as soon as another model was introduced which I liked, but which came from another region. In short, I had become an avid collector.

Tuck Shop – my first cottage

Since that first purchase in 1985 I have gathered together a considerable amount of information about the cottages: the mould and colour changes to the models; special commissions; limited editions; and so on. Having discovered these various facts, I began to wonder whether the thousands of other Lilliput Lane collectors were aware of the fascinating and intriguing insights into the models that Lilliput Lane have produced. Did they know that four – possibly five – versions of Sussex Mill existed? Were they aware of the ladders and crosses on Adobe Village? Had they ever seen Penny Lanes? And how many of them had the series of clowns in their collection?

The more I thought about this, the more convinced I became of the need for me to broaden and amplify the information I had, with a view to publishing it. However, having decided to go ahead with the book it was then that the hard work really began, as I needed to obtain the information that was missing and verify the information that I already had.

To achieve these objectives I had meetings with numerous Lilliput Lane enthusiasts and collectors and we had many lengthy chats and discussions about the models, the versions available, and the related items which are now becoming collectable such as brochures and other promotional material. Those meetings also confirmed my belief that the wealth of material would be beneficial to other collectors.

I have endeavoured to make the information in the book as accurate as possible, and I hope that it will be of interest and benefit to both new and established collectors. However, there are some models where either I have not been able to obtain a photograph or where the information is not as detailed as I would have liked. If any Lilliput Lane collectors have any information, photographs or comments which can help to make this book even more comprehensive, then please do not hesitate to contact me at the publisher's address.

Annette Power
December 1994

Discovering Lilliput Lane Cottages

One of the best ways to learn about Lilliput Lane past and present is to visit their Collectors Centre at Skirsgill, near Penrith, Cumbria. The lure of the company museum, showroom and studio tour, set in spectacular Lake District scenery, draws collectors from all over the world and they return home even more knowledgeable and enthusiastic about their chosen hobby. The centre is only open to members of the Lilliput Lane Collectors Club and advance booking is required for the studio tour.

Vernacular Architecture

The journey north from London passes through many of the areas celebrated in the Lilliput Lane collection and, if time allows, it is worth a detour to explore the charming Cotswold villages, with cottages built of the local honey-coloured stone, or the black and white timber-framed buildings of the Midlands, aptly described as 'Magpie' style.

Comparing the original buildings with the authentically detailed Lilliput Lane models helps illustrate how the different character of towns and villages have been shaped by the availability of building materials and the development of specialist local crafts, such as thatching or pargeting. Indeed, part of the fun of collecting Lilliput Lane Cottages is having a greater appreciation of vernacular architecture, described by company founder David Tate as 'buildings built by the people for the people with the materials that lay around them'.

Starting the Company

Travelling north-west into the Lake District, the landscape changes dramatically and hill farms, hewn from local stone, cling to exposed mountain slopes. Thousands of visitors come to this area every year to marvel at the majesty of the scenery and enjoy the climbing and water-sports, and it was here that David Tate decided to base his new cottage company in 1982.

Workshops were found at Skirsgill, near Penrith, in the converted stables of an old mansion house and somewhat basic accommodation was provided at Rose Cottage for David, his wife and two teenage daughters. The whole family worked round the clock to establish the business and at night they would retire to their cold, damp home.

The Collectors Centre

It is hard to imagine the Tate family's spartan existence arriving at the Lilliput Lane workshops today. When the new Collectors Centre was created in 1991, Rose Cottage was converted into a charming little museum and showroom set in a cobbled courtyard, complete with Victorian lamp-posts and a traditional red telephone box, which was

The old coach house at Skirsgill, which is now Gulliver's Pantry

rescued from certain destruction. The old coach house for the Skirsgill estate now forms Gulliver's Pantry, which provides welcome refreshments after a tour of the studios. Having started with 800 square feet of workshop space and six staff, the company now dominates the stable block and has expanded to several different sites in Cumbria with some 700 employees.

David Tate

Some collectors may be fortunate enough to meet David Tate during their visit as he is still actively involved in the running of the company, that is when he is not travelling the world with his audio-visual show, presenting the Lilliput Lane cottages to an ever-growing international audience. It was his energy and determination that got the company off the ground and he sustained its growth with a combination of talents, including a strong visual memory and exceptional engineering skills acquired in the army.

His speciality was fibreglass moulding and he developed a new technique for moulding small, intricately detailed cottages in one piece, unlike traditional production methods in the ceramic industry which require sculptures to be assembled from several mould parts. He was so convinced of the potential of his new cottage models that he sold his house to get started and, despite constant cash-flow problems in the early years, he has succeeded in building up a company which has won the highly-coveted Queen's Award for Export and Achievement and the lion's share of awards at the international collectables shows.

In 1988 he was honoured personally with the MBE and since November 1993 the company has been publicly quoted on the London Stock Exchange – a remarkable catalogue of achievements in just 12 years.

Rose Cottage Museum

The results of his endeavours can be

seen in the Rose Cottage museum, which displays a wide range of Lilliput Lane Cottages past and present. The collection began in 1982 with fourteen cottages modelled by David himself. Many were inspired by the vernacular buildings which he had grown to love in the Lake District and his native Yorkshire, for example, Lakeside House and Dale Farm. Rural Hampshire, where he had lived for some years, suggested Honeysuckle Cottage and April Cottage.

A few models from the launch collection are now extremely rare as they were not made for very long, notably Old Mine, which was discontinued after ten months with only 200 pieces produced, and Drapers which was withdrawn at the same time with only 360 pieces made in two different colour treatments.

Technical Developments

Many modelling and colour changes were made to the cottages in the early years as David gradually improved production techniques as well as the body and paint formulations.

The first important development in 1983 was the use of glass-reinforced plastic moulds instead of the traditional plaster type and this enabled much more complex sculptures to be reproduced. Originally a basic Crystacel plaster was used for the body of the cottages, but this was too light weight and brittle and in 1984 he perfected Amorphite, a much harder and stronger material suitable for reproducing more intricate detail.

The paints also needed to be improved as the original colours were liable to fade in bright sunlight. After much experimentation, in 1984 David introduced new earth-based pigments which could be applied in colour washes, enhancing all the different textures of the model, and these were reformulated in 1990 to make them even more transparent and brighter.

Not one to rest on his laurels, David is constantly looking for new ways to improve processes and techniques and his Research and Development department is a hive of activity. For obvious reasons this building is not part of the studio tour nor is the Modelling department where the artists work on the future cottage introductions. However, the Lilliput Lane tour guides explain the nature of all the 'behind the scenes' stages before conducting visitors around the various production processes.

Behind the Scenes

David Tate and his team of artists travel many thousands of miles each year searching out suitable subject matter for the Lilliput Lane collection and they have built up an extensive library of reference books and photographs of vernacular architecture.

Once a specific building has been chosen for reproduction the detailed research begins. It is photographed from every angle and sketches are made on location to capture the unique atmosphere of the property and its surroundings. Back in the studio, the sculptor produces lots of interpretative sketches, emphasizing certain features, before preparing the final working drawing. The scale they work to for the finished sculpture is generally 1/76th of the original building.

The sculptors work with a specially formulated wax and they manipulate this warm, malleable material into the basic shape of the building before carving the detail with an assortment of tools.

Dental instruments have proved very useful for achieving the right texture for tiny details, such as bricks or window panes, which are carefully cut into the walls. If the building requires roofing slates or tiles, these are cut from a thin sheet of wax and individually applied – a very time-consuming task.

Many pieces have elaborate gardens which will be 'planted' painstakingly with intricately sculpted bushes and flowers. The artists all study the different flower seasons to ensure their gardens are accurately interpreted.

Generally it takes the sculptors a minimum of two weeks to create a finished wax for the general range, complex

prestige or limited edition pieces take much longer.

Touring Production

The wax original is destroyed in the mould-making process so there is no margin for error in the skilled tooling department. First of all a solid block mould is produced in silicone rubber and several resin copies or 'masters' of the original are cast. The master is then coated with a thin layer of plastic, and fibreglass is carefully laid on top of this to form a multi-part case.

After hardening the fibreglass case is removed in sections and the plastic is peeled away from its interior and the outside of the master model. Now, when the case is re-assembled around the master, there is a narrow gap which is injected with silicone rubber to form the finished mould.

Finally, a secondary case is made to support the mould during casting and, after thorough testing, all these tools are transferred to the production mould-making department to make lots of silicone rubber working moulds.

Visitors to Lilliput Lane can also watch the casting and de-moulding processes which have been refined over

Smoothing the base of a cottage

many years. Liquid Amorphite is poured into the silicone rubber moulds, which are supported by back-up moulds whilst they are vibrated at low frequency to remove air bubbles.

As the Amorphite is setting, the base of the cast is levelled and this will be ground smooth later. It takes just over half an hour for the Amorphite to set to the required degree and the silicone mould is then removed from the back-up and stripped from the cast. It is not as easy as it looks. De-moulding is a very skilled job and great care must be taken to ensure no tall chimneys or spires are broken off.

Many of the craftsmen and women performing these delicate operations seem very young and David Tate is proud of the fact that the average age in the company is only 25. The various Lilliput Lane studios in Cumbria are major employers of youthful talent and, after intensive training and all the relevant work experience, many school leavers are promoted to responsible positions at an early age.

Before the casts of the cottages are completely hard, the fettlers will remove any unwanted remnants of plaster which remain in deep recesses and the piece is allowed to dry for 24 hours before being dipped in a coloured sealant. The colour of the dip is dependent on the original building materials and visitors can see samples of all the base colours and the different effects they produce. A more prolonged drying period in a

Fettling, where any unwanted pieces of plaster are removed

de-humidifying chamber follows and the piece is then ready for painting.

For many visitors, this is the most exciting department. The carousels of specially formulated paint create a riot of colour and there is something magical about seeing the cottages come to life with the deft touches of the painter's brush. The intense concentration of the artists creates an intimate atmosphere, which is punctuated only by the gasps of delight from collectors as they see their favourite piece or a future introduction being decorated. Each painter specialises in just a few different models which enables them to work as efficiently as possible. For reference, they have a master copy which has been created after hours of experimentation by the chief colourist. Sometimes more than thirty different effects are tried out in the Colouring department before a final choice is made.

During the various stages of production, there have been several inspections and sub-standard models are destroyed before they reach the final quality control department. The piece is scrutinised once again and, if satisfactory, is finished with green baize and despatched to Lilliput Lane stockists all over the world.

The Current Range
After an inspirational tour, most collectors want to return to Rose Cottage to buy souvenirs of their visit – perhaps even a piece they have seen being decorated. The choice is endless as there are representative buildings from every part of the UK – magpie buildings and mills

from the Midlands, remote farms and village schools from the North, thatched cottages and pubs from the South-East and seaside cottages from the South-West. Wales is represented by tiny slate-roofed cottages and chapels, Scotland by castles and tenements, and Ireland by crofts and village stores.

The Lilliput Lane studios have also gone further afield for inspiration in response to their growing international audience. In 1986 David Tate and sculptor Tom Raine drove around Northern Europe seeking inspiration for the German collection, which was followed by the French and Dutch collections in 1990 and 1991 respectively. Originally the national collections were only sold in their respective countries but now they are available in the UK.

A log cabin and an adobe village were early, but short lived, introductions to a US series and in 1989 a new direction was taken when Ray Day, one of America's top artists, was commissioned to produce the American Landmarks collection especially for the thousands of Lilliput Lane collectors in the USA.

For collectors conscious of space and budget limitations, a range of miniature cottages, less than 3 inches tall, was added to the range in 1993. The cottages in the Classics collection, as it is known, were all inspired by the picturesque village in Blaise Hamlet. Miniature cottages, blanketed in snow, have

Painting: each artist specialises in a few different models

Painting: close attention to detail and a steady hand is required

also proved very popular as Christmas gifts and no doubt many new collections will grow from these seasonal 'seeds'.

Building a Collection
Many Lilliput Lane collections grow from chance gifts and, as the delighted recipient gradually succumbs to the infinite charms of the cottages, new purchases follow, sometimes in quick succession! Other collections start from souvenirs purchased at famous British beauty spots and then the fun continues as holidays are spent travelling the country looking for the original buildings which inspired each cottage.

Some collectors become interested in cottages because of their personal associations, for example they have lived in a thatched cottage or been married in a church with the same name or appearance as a Lilliput Lane model. Whatever their starting point, all collectors share the nostalgia for the past which is evoked by all the buildings in the Lilliput range.

It is not unusual for very large collections to be created in comparatively short periods of time as the enthusiasm blossoms. Cabinets and display shelves are built apace and before long it is necessary to convert the spare room or the garage into a showroom! For those aspiring to form a complete collection, it is advisable to keep up with all the introductions to the current range, as, once they are discontinued, they can become very elusive. Lilliput Lane regularly re-

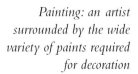

Painting: an artist surrounded by the wide variety of paints required for decoration

tire pieces from the range as David Tate explains, 'We care about collectors and we want to maintain the collectability of our cottages by controlling the numbers rather than just exploiting them.'

Some keen collectors will cross continents in search of retired pieces and stiff competition has led to some meteoric price rises for rare pieces on the secondary market. Auctions of retired pieces have been held at the Lilliput Lane Annual Fair and several specialist dealers are now catering for the demand for discontinued cottages on both sides of the Atlantic. The highest prices are paid for David Tate's first designs with very short production runs. Early versions of cottages with modelling and colour variations also attract a lot of interest. It is hard to believe when the hammer comes down on three- or four-figure prices that the early cottages originally retailed for around £2.50!

Nowadays complex prestige pieces start around £100 in the current price lists, so many collectors need to budget for these special pieces. However, a high price is not a deterrent for spectacular designs as was proved in 1989 with St Peter's Cove, the company's most ambitious and challenging sculpture. The limited edition of 3,000 pieces was sold out within six months and it now changes hands for considerably more than its issue price.

Special commissions with limited distribution, such as the Seven Dwarfs Cottage made for Disney World in 1986 or Mayflower House which was exclu-

Skirsgill, the home of the Lilliput Lane Collectors Club

sive to the USA in 1989–90, are hard to find today, particularly in the UK. No doubt Counting House Corner, which was produced in a limited edition of 3,093 to mark the company's flotation on the London Stock Exchange, will also be very sought after in the future as the edition was oversubscribed by over 7,000 applications and it was only offered to UK Club members.

The Collectors Club was founded in 1986 and membership grew rapidly from 500 in the first month to over 70,000 members worldwide today. Subscribers receive the informative quarterly magazine *Gulliver's World* as well as annual joining gifts and exclusive cottage offers. Some of the first Club editions such as Crendon Manor and Yew Tree Farm now command high premiums and even past free gifts fetch surprising prices, in particular Packhorse Bridge and Little Lost Dog.

For a brief period the company dabbled in figurative models of clowns and these are now desirable along with the study of Gulliver, the hero of Jonathan Swift's travel tale from which the Lilliput Lane name was taken. Little advertising signs used to promote the company name in retail stores are now sought after and serious collectors are also seeking out all the early sales literature.

One very special collectors piece which all visitors to the Collectors Centre are eligible to purchase is the model of Rose Cottage, Skirsgill, where the Lilliput Lane story began. As only a small proportion of the worldwide Club membership has the chance to make this 'pilgrimage' to the Lake District and few would part with this exclusive souvenir of a memorable day, it is a much coveted collectable.

Further Reading

The Cottages of Lilliput Lane, Deborah Scott, Portfolio Press Corporation, 1991

Gulliver's World, published quarterly by the Lilliput Lane Collectors Club

Lilliput Lane Collectors Club

Details of membership are available from the following offices or from your local Lilliput Lane stockist:

Australia

Lilliput Lane Collectors Club, 62–64 Oakover Road, Preston, PO Box 282, Victoria 3072

New Zealand

Lilliput Lane Collectors Club, Hampton Sales Limited, PO Box 1140, Emerson Street, Napier

USA

9052 Old Annapolis Road, Columbia, MD 21045

UK and other countries

Lilliput Lane Collectors Club, Skirsgill, Penrith, Cumbria CA11 0DP, England

Other Collectables from Lilliput Lane

To the majority of collectors the name Lilliput Lane is synonymous with the miniature sculptures of cottages, castles and other buildings which can be seen at most china, collectables and gift shops, and it is the descriptions of those models which make up the majority of the information in this book.

However, Lilliput Lane did produce other items which should not be overlooked, and descriptions of these items are given below.

Land of Legend

Portraying a world of fantasy and myth, a collection of models was introduced in the mid-1980s under the title Land of Legend. Of particular interest to Lilliput Lane cottage collectors were the castles included in the Land of Legend range. Six castles were introduced:

Castle of the Exiled Prince
Castle of the Golden Chalice
Castle of the Ransomed King
Castle of the Red Knight
Castle of the Sleeping Princess
Sorcerer's Retreat.

A seventh castle, Wizard's Tower, was introduced in 1988.

Two other castles, Schloss Neuschwanstein and Schloss Rheinjungfrau, were introduced in 1988 each in a limited edition of 1,500 pieces.

In the same way that Bridge House and Packhorse Bridge had been produced as promotional dealer signs for use by retailers of Lilliput Lane cottages, so there was a promotional dealer sign for Land of Legend retailers. Called Dennis the Dragon, the model was available to retailers from 1986–87.

Further information on the Land of Legend models is given later in the book.

Plaques

In the late 1980s Lilliput Lane produced a range of wall plaques. More than forty-five plaques were produced covering a variety of subjects, some of them were framed, others were unframed.

The collections produced were:

Countryside Scene Collection
Bottle Kiln
Cornish Tin Mine
Country Inn
Cumbrian Farmhouse
Lighthouse
Norfolk Windmill
Oast House
Old Smithy
Parish Church
Post Office
Village School
Watermill

English Collection (framed)
Ashdown Hall
Battle View
Catslide Cottage
Coombe Cot
Fell View
Flintfields
Huntingdon House
Jubilee Lodge
Stourside
Treven Cove

Irish Collection (framed)
Ballyteeg House
Crockuna Croft
Pearse's Cottage
Shannons Bank

Lakeland Bridge Collection
Aira Force
Ashness Bridge
Birks Bridge
Bridge House
Hartsop Packhorse
Stockley Bridge

London Collection
Big Ben
Buckingham Palace
Piccadilly Circus
Tower Bridge
Tower of London
Trafalgar Square

Scottish Collection (framed)
Barra Blackhouse
Fife Ness
Kyle Point
Preston Oat Mill

Unframed
Cobble Combe Cottage (medium)
Lower Brockhampton (large)
Somerset Springtime (large)
Stoneywell Lea (small)
Wishing Well Cottage (medium)
Woodside Farm (small)

The unframed plaques were produced in varying sizes, with some being small, some medium and some large; the framed plaques had a frame size of 7½ in. by 9 in. (19 cm by 23 cm).

All of the plaques were withdrawn during 1992 and 1993. They do not seem to have been particularly popular and most can still be obtained at retail outlets.

Plates
Following on from his work on the American Landmarks collection, in 1990 Ray Day designed a series of five plates related to the American Landmarks. The plates were commissioned

Backstamp on the Country Church plate from the series commissioned by Gift Link Inc.

by Gift Link Inc., from Columbia, Maryland, in the USA, and were limited editions of 5,000 pieces. The five subjects were Country Church, Meramic Caverns, Perennial Favourites, Riverside Chapel and Rock City. The plates were not available in the UK, and only two (Country Church and Riverside Chapel) are still available in the USA, the others now being fully subscribed.

In 1994, Lilliput Lane produced their first-ever collectors plate for Franklin Mint. Entitled Wishing Well Cottage, the 8-in. (20¼-cm) diameter plate was limited to the number of orders received by the closing date of 15 October 1994.

Memorabilia

Some collectors have expanded their area of collecting beyond the models themselves to include other related Lilliput Lane material. Besides the main advertising and promotional items such as dealer signs, point of sale items, brochures and other sales literature, many collectors also collect and display other 'gifts' which can be obtained at Annual Fairs, special events, and in-store promotions.

Some examples of the souvenirs and memorabilia available is shown later and includes a brooch issued to those who had been Collectors Club members for five years.

Dating Lilliput Lane Models

There are three methods of dating a Lilliput Lane model: the design of the label on the base, the certificate and the design of the packaging, and the company backstamp.

Labels

The label on the base can be used to identify the approximate age of a model. In the early days from 1982 to 1984, two types of label were used, one had a brown border and the other had a blue border. In 1985 the design of the label was changed with the company name featured prominently in the centre of the label. Examples of the various types of labels used on the models are shown later in the book.

Packaging

The design of the packaging has evolved during the years since 1982 and should the model still have its original packaging then this can aid or even confirm the age of the model. Examples of the changes in the design of the box are shown later in the book.

Should a box be required for a model, then it is possible to purchase one of the current boxes through the retailer for a small charge.

Collectors always wonder whether a model is more valuable when it has its original box and its certificate with it.

With regard to certificates, certainly a limited edition or Collectors Club model should have its relevant certificate to show its provenance, and in the case of numbered editions a certificate is vital. However, with the other models many of the older ones did not have certificates with them when the model was produced.

Obviously, in an ideal world every collector would like to purchase a retired model complete with its original packaging and certificate. However, as this is not always possible, each collector must decide whether the model they wish to buy warrants the price being asked, or whether they should wait until they can purchase a model which is complete with the box and certificate. A model which does have its original box and certificate certainly will have added attractions to some collectors than a model on its own.

Backstamps

Backstamps are of great importance when dating a model and the following illustrations show the various backstamps used since 1982. The backstamps are referenced alphabetically, but note that the letter I is not used in the sequence. These backstamps are also referred to in the descriptions of the individual models later in the book.

Backstamp A

A- LILLIPUT LANE

(1ˢᵀ)

STAMP INTO MOULD

LILLIPUT LANE

Backstamp B

B- LILLIPUT LANE
COPYRIGHT
1982
U.K.

(2ᴺᴰ)

STAMP INTO MOULD

© LILLIPUT LANE LTD.
COPYRIGHT 1982 UK

Backstamp C

C- LILLIPUT LANE
COPYRIGHT
1983
U.K.

(3ᴿᴰ)

STAMP INTO MOULD

© LILLIPUT LANE LTD.
COPYRIGHT 1983 UK

Backstamp D

D- LILLIPUT LANE
COPYRIGHT
1984
U.K.

(4ᵀᴴ)

STAMP INTO MOULD

© LILLIPUT LANE LTD.
COPYRIGHT 1984 UK

Backstamp E

E- LILLIPUT LANE
1985

(5ᵀᴴ)

STAMP INTO MOULD

© Lilliput Lane 1985

Backstamp F

F- LILLIPUT LANE
1986

(6TH)

STAMP INTO MOULD

Backstamp G

G- LILLIPUT LANE
1987

(7TH)

STAMP INTO MOULD

Backstamp H

H- LILLIPUT LANE
1988

(8TH)

STAMP INTO MOULD

Backstamp J

J- LILLIPUT LANE
1989

(9TH)

STAMP INTO MOULD

Backstamp K

K- LILLIPUT LANE
1990

(10TH)

QUITE FLAT IN
APPEARANCE

Backstamp L

L- LILLIPUT LANE
1991

(11 TH)

QUITE FLAT IN
APPEARANCE

Backstamp M

M- LILLIPUT LANE
1992

(12 TH)

FLAT LETTERS -
STANDS OUT A LITTLE -
NO SPECIFIC SHAPE -

Backstamp N

N- LILLIPUT LANE
1993

(13 TH)

STRAIGHT LETTERING -
STANDS OUT A LOT MORE -
NO SPECIFIC SHAPE -

Backstamp O

O- LILLIPUT LANE
1994

(14 TH)

SLIGHTLY IMPRESSED
LETTERS -
STANDS OUT -
NO SPECIFIC SHAPE -

Studley Royal Collection

At the time of the book going to press limited information was becoming available about a new collection being introduced by Lilliput Lane. Known as the Studley Royal Collection it depicts the buildings to be seen at the well-known country estate. Initially the collection will only be available in the USA.

Studley Royal, near Ripon in Yorkshire, was created between 1716 and 1781 by John Aislabie and his son William. One of the few great 18th-century gardens to still exist in much of its original form, the Aislabie's design made very good use of water, lawns and buildings against a background of trees.

John Aislabie inherited Studley in 1699, at a time when he was actively involved in public life. However, although he had become Chancellor of the Exchequer in 1718, the 'South Sea Bubble' disaster ruined his career, and upon returning to Yorkshire in 1720 he devoted all of his time and efforts to the creation of Studley gardens.

From 1716 to 1730 the layout was developed and constructed with canals and ponds being built, embankments and ramps designed around the lawned areas, and trees planted.

After 1732 work began on the buildings, and between 1732 and 1742 the Temple of Fame, Temple of Piety, the Banqueting House, the Octagon Tower, the Rustic Bridge, Grotto and Serpentine Tunnel were constructed.

When John Aislabie died in 1742 the main work of the garden had been completed, however the crowning glory of his scheme – the inclusion of Fountains Abbey – was not attained until 1768 when William succeeded in purchasing Fountains Abbey and Fountains Hall from his neighbour.

Lilliput Lane began the introduction of the Studley Royal Collection in 1994. Five models were announced: Banqueting House, Fountains Abbey,

Octagon Tower, 4 in./10 cm high, due to be released in 1995

*Banqueting House, 3¼ in./8 cm high,
due to be released in 1995*

Octagon Tower, St Mary's Church, and Temple of Piety. At present the collection is only available in the USA, with St Mary's Church and Temple of Piety released in July 1994 and the other subjects expected to be released in January 1995. Fountains Abbey will be a limited edition of 3,500 pieces; the others will be limited editions of 5,000 pieces each. It is anticipated that the models will be generally available elsewhere twelve months after the launch in the USA.

How to Use this Book

The book gives individual details of the wide range of models produced by Lilliput Lane since the company began in 1982. The models are in alphabetical sequence and for each model details are given of the name, the collection it belongs to, a brief history and architectural details of the building upon which the model is based (if applicable), information about the Lilliput Lane model, the year that the model was introduced and the year it was retired (if the model is no longer current), the height, the number of versions produced, the backstamps carried by the model during its production period, the current value (in £ sterling and US dollars) of the model on the secondary market (if the model is still in production then the recommended retail price [RRP] applies).

The £ sterling and US dollar prices are not straight conversions at currency rates; the prices are different because various factors can affect the secondary market values, for instance a model which was only available in the USA may not command as high a value in the USA as it does in the UK (Seven Dwarfs Cottage is an example of this).

Regarding the production dates for Lilliput Lane Collectors Club models, it should be remembered that the dates of the Club year differ between the UK and the USA; the UK Club year runs from March to the following February, whereas the USA Club year runs from May to the following April. Whenever the months of introduction and retirement are mentioned for Collectors Club models the UK Club year has been used, for USA Club members the introduction and retirement will be two months later.

One final comment about secondary market values. A wide variety of sources have been used to establish the prices given in this handbook, and all of the prices given are for perfect examples which are not damaged; for damaged or restored models the price should be reduced accordingly. All of the prices are intended purely as a guide to collectors as to what they should expect to pay for a particular model. You will find models priced higher, you will find models priced lower; remember – at the end of the day the model is only worth its value to you.

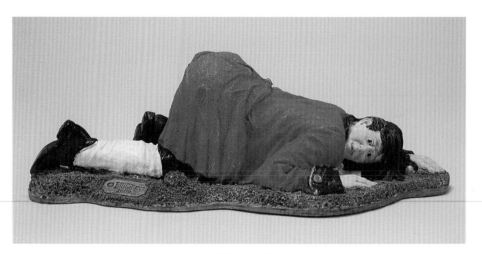

Gulliver 1986

*Produced from February 1986 to December 1986, the initial production
pieces had the backstamp positioned on the front; however, at some
point the backstamp was repositioned on the rear*

Lower Brockhampton Wall Plaque

*Riverside Chapel and Country Church plates
shown with their respective models*

A selection of souvenirs and other memorabilia

Lilliput Lane Models

Aan de Amstel

Netherlands Collection

Aberford Gate

Special Events

Aan de Amstel (On the Amstel) is typical of the buildings to be found in the city of Amsterdam, which takes its name from the first dam to be built across the River Amstel in the 13th century. Dam Square became the heart of the city and many important municipal buildings were situated there.

Released in February 1991, and similar to De Diamantair apart from the colouring, Aan de Amstel is still current.

Produced: 1991–
Height: 5¾ in./14½ cm
Versions: 1
Backstamp: L
Current value: £RRP ($RRP)

Aberford Gate was based upon the gate house to the Gascoigne Almshouses at Aberford in Yorkshire.

The model was launched in September 1993 at the Collectors Meeting at Harewood House, and was only available at that meeting and at the other special events and collectors meetings held from September 1993–September 1994.

Produced: 1993–94
Height: 3/3-8 in./8½ cm
Versions: 1
Backstamp: N
Current value: £55–65 ($100–200)

Acorn Cottage

English Collection – South-East

Acorn Cottage was among the original fourteen cottages that launched Lilliput Lane. The cottage, which is located not far from the London–Portsmouth road, would originally have been thatched.

Introduced in September 1982, the cottage was restyled a year later, when it became larger and a boulder at the front was removed. On the earlier version the roof tiling was less refined and the foliage around the base was not as detailed and as well-positioned.

Acorn Cottage was retired in December 1987.

Produced: 1982–87
Height: 2 in./5 cm; version 1 smaller
Versions: 2
Backstamp: A, B, D
Current value:
   Version 1 – £300–375 ($600–700)
   Version 2 – £50–70 ($100–120)

*Front view:
version 1 (left);
version 2 (right)*

*Side view:
version 2 (left);
version 1 (right)*

*Back view:
version 2 (left);
version 1 (right)*

Adobe Church

American Collection – 1st Series

Introduced in October 1984, Adobe Church was one of the fourteen buildings in the American Collection – 1st Series. The series was not very popular, and all of the models now have a high rarity value. Only 475 pieces were produced of Adobe Church, which was retired in October 1985.

Produced: 1984–85
Height: 2¾ in./7 cm
Versions: 1
Backstamp: D
Current value: £350–400 ($450–550)

Adobe Village

American Collection – 1st Series

Although it was only in production for a year following its introduction in October 1984, two versions of Adobe Village were produced. The original version had three free-standing crosses above the entrance door of the church,

Version 1, with three crosses above the church door and ladders resting against the houses

4

Version 2, with only one cross above the church door and no ladders resting against the houses

and three ladders resting against some of the houses at the various levels; the second version had only one cross above the church door and did not have any ladders resting against the houses. Only 225 pieces had been produced of Adobe Village when it was retired in October 1985.

Produced: 1984–85
Height: 4¾ in./12 cm
Versions: 2
Backstamp: C, D
Current value:
   Version 1 – £550–600 ($750–900)
   Version 2 – £550–600 ($750–900)

Alphonse

Miscellaneous

Little is known about the set of five clowns which were produced between 1983 and 1984.

   Alphonse has recorded sales of less than 100 pieces.

Produced: 1983–84
Height: 5–6 in./12½–15 cm
Versions: 1
Backstamp: A
Current value: £550–650 ($1,500+)

Alte Schmiede

German Collection

Alte Schmiede (Old Smithy) is one of the famous buildings in the Bavarian 16th-century town of Rothenburg on the River Tauber.

Introduced in February 1992, this model is still current.

Produced: 1992–
Height: 4½ in./11½ cm
Versions: 1
Backstamp: M
Current value: £RRP ($RRP)

Anne Hathaway's Cottage

English Collection – Midlands

Located at Shottery, a mile to the west of Stratford-upon-Avon, Anne Hathaway's Cottage is in fact a 12-roomed thatched house. In the parlour is the uncomfortable bench, or settle, where Shakespeare is thought to have courted his future bride.

Based upon the timber-framed cottage, this model was produced in three versions. First introduced in February

6

1983, the original version, with the name of the cottage embossed in white on the front of the base, is the rarest. In September 1983 it was remodelled without the name on the base, and in September 1984 was remodelled yet again with a larger chimney. Anne Hathaway's Cottage (not to be confused with Anne Hathaway's Cottage 1989), was retired in December 1988.

Produced: 1983–88
Height: 2½ in./6¼ cm
Versions: 3
Backstamp: A, C, D
Current value:
  Version 1 – £700–800 ($1,500–1,750)
  Version 2 – £150–180 ($350+)
  Version 3 – £60–75 ($75–100)

Anne Hathaway's Cottage 1989

English Collection – Midlands

Anne Hathaway's Cottage 1989 should not be confused with its predecessor Anne Hathaway's Cottage.

Introduced in February 1989, this model has a cottage garden at the front and has more warmth than its predecessor. The model is still current.

Produced: 1989–
Height: 3¼ in./8 cm
Versions: 1
Backstamp: J
Current value: £RRP ($RRP)

Anne of Cleves

English Collection – South-East

Modelled upon the manor house in Ditchling, Sussex, which Henry VIII gave to his fourth wife Anne of Cleves upon their divorce after only six months of marriage, this model was introduced in July 1991 and is still current.

Produced: 1991–
Height: 5¾ in./14 cm
Versions: 1
Backstamp: L
Current value: £RRP ($RRP)

Applejack Cottage

English Collection – South-West

Applejack Cottage can be found close to the famous village of Beaulieu in Hampshire. Built in the 18th century, the cottage is a good example of traditional cottage architecture featuring stone and thatch.

Introduced in February 1994, this model is still current.

Produced: 1994–
Height: 2½ in./6¼ cm
Versions: 1
Backstamp: O
Current value: £RRP ($RRP)

April Cottage
English Collection – South-East

April Cottage is situated in central Hampshire, not far from the main road between London and Southampton. Built around 1600, the cottage still retains its thatched roof.

Introduced in September 1982, the model was restyled in August 1983 when it was made larger and the three-pot chimney was changed to a two-pot chimney. The thatched roof and beams on the original version were less refined than the second version; also, the base was thicker and gave more of a 'cut' look than the 'finished' look of the restyled version. The model was retired in December 1989.

Produced: 1982–89
Height: 2 in./5 cm; version 1 smaller
Versions: 2
Backstamp: A, D
Current value:
    Version 1 – £350–400 ($600–750)
    Version 2 – £40–60 ($100–125)

Version 1, showing the three-pot chimney

Version 2, larger and with the two-pot chimney

Armada House

English Collection – Midlands

Armada House is typical of the buildings found in rural Northamptonshire, on the eastern edge of the Cotswold stone belt.

Introduced in February 1991, the model is still current.

Produced: 1991–
Height: 4¼ in./
  10½ cm
Versions: 1
Backstamp: L
Current value: £RRP
  ($RRP)

Ash Nook

English Collection – South-East

Typical of the properties which would have originally been inhabited by the village artisans of Hertfordshire, Ash Nook is built from timber framing and in-filled with plaster and brick; timber cladding gives protection from the sharp winter winds blowing in from the east.

The model was introduced in February 1989 and is still current.

Produced: 1989–
Height: 3 in./7½ cm
Versions: 1
Backstamp: J
Current value: £RRP ($RRP)

Ashberry 92

Exclusive

This cottage was produced exclusively for Lilliput Lane collectors who had booked and attended the Lilliput Lane Dinner at the 1992 South Bend Show in the USA. Unlike other models produced for the South Bend Show, this model was not released in a different colourway/backstamp for sale at other Lilliput Lane events. It is believed that between 500 and 600 pieces were produced.

Produced: July–September 1992
Height: 3½ in./9 cm
Versions: 1
Backstamp: M
Current value: £275–350 ($300–350)

L'Auberge d'Armorique

French Collection

L'Auberge d'Armorique (Armorique Guest House) can be found on the rugged north coast of Brittany, and is typical of the buildings in the area.

The model, which is the second largest in the French Collection, was introduced in September 1990 and is still current.

Produced: 1990–
Height: 5½ in./14 cm
Versions: 1
Backstamp: K
Current value: £RRP ($RRP)

Autumn Hues

A Year in an English Garden

The launch of this cottage, in July 1994, together with its companion cottage Winter's Wonder, introduced an interesting new concept to the collecting of cottages, where the same cottage is portrayed to show the way in which the seasons of the year can alter the appearance of the cottage.

The seasonal portrayals are: spring (Spring Glory), summer (Summer Impressions), autumn (Autumn Hues) and winter (Winter's Wonder). The cottages for spring and summer are due to be released in 1995.

Each cottage in the 4-model series has with it a stamp, and all four stamps can be redeemed for a certificate of ownership.

Produced: 1994–
Height: 3-3/8 in./8½ cm
Versions: 1
Backstamp: O
Current value: £RRP ($RRP)

Ballykerne Croft

Irish Collection

Located in the Maumturk Mountains of County Galway, Ballykerne Croft is built firm against the Atlantic weather.

Introduced in February 1989 as the first model in the Irish Collection, Ballykerne Croft is still currently available.

Produced: 1989–
Height: 2½ in./6¼ cm
Versions: 1
Backstamp: J
Current value: £RRP
   ($RRP)

Bay View

English Collection – South-East

Bay View is typical of the many brick and flint cottages to be found on the North Norfolk coast by Burnham Market, overlooking Brancaster Bay.

Introduced in February 1986, the model was retired in December 1988.

Produced: 1986–88
Height: 2½ in./6¼ cm
Versions: 1
Backstamp: F
Current value: £70–90
   ($100–125)

Beacon Heights

English Collection – Northern

Based upon a mock-Tudor house perched on a hillside in Northumberland, Beacon Heights is typical of properties built during the Victorian era when architects endeavoured to emulate the styles of earlier periods.

Introduced in February 1987, Beacon Heights was retired in July 1992.

Produced: 1987–92
Height: 5¼ in./13½ cm
Versions: 1
Backstamp: G
Current value: £100–120 ($175–200)

Beehive Cottage

English Collection – Midlands

Beehive Cottage was introduced in February 1989 and is still current, although it is due to be retired in March 1995.

Produced: 1989–95
Height: 3¾ in./9½ cm
Versions: 1
Backstamp: J
Current value: £RRP ($RRP)

Begijnhof
Netherlands Collection

Begijnhof (The Almshouse) was built to provide accommodation for the deserving poor, such as widows. The main house consisted of meeting rooms which were used by the Regents (the city's ruling class who were the almshouses governors), and behind the main house was a courtyard surrounded by small cottages.

Introduced in February 1991, Begijnhof is similar to De Pepermolen apart from the colouring, and is still current.

Produced: 1991–
Height: 4¾ in./12 cm
Versions: 1
Backstamp: L
Current value: £RRP ($RRP)

B

La Bergerie du Perigord
French Collection

La Bergerie du Perigord (Perigord Farmhouse) is a typical small farm found in the Dordogne region of France. Built of stone on various levels, the ground floor provides storage room and shelter for animals, while the other floors are occupied by the farmer and his family. Introduced in September 1990, the model is still current.

Produced: 1990–
Height: 5 in./12½ cm
Versions: 1
Backstamp: K
Current value: £RRP ($RRP)

Bermuda Cottage

Exclusive

Bermuda Cottage was a special commission by a company in Bermuda called The Britannia. Introduced in September 1985, the cottage was initially available in three colours: blue, pink and yellow. Although the model was withdrawn in 1988 it was then re-issued in the same year.

Bermuda Cottage carries a plain printed label with details of the cottage, and although three colour variations were produced, the blue colourway is the most difficult to acquire.

Bermuda Cottage was finally withdrawn in July 1991.

Produced: 1985–91
Height: 2 in./5 cm
Versions: 3 colour variations
Backstamp: E
Current value:
  Blue – £120–150 ($250–300)
  Pink – £80–100 ($125–150)
  Yellow – £80–100 ($125–150)

Birdlip Bottom

English Collection – Midlands

Birdlip Bottom is an early 18th-century thatched cottage situated at the foot of the Cotswolds in rural Gloucestershire.

Introduced in July 1993, the model is still currently available.

Produced: 1993–
Height: 3¼ in./8 cm
Versions: 1
Backstamp: N
Current value: £RRP ($RRP)

The Birdsong

American Landmarks

The Birdsong is based upon the American Mid-west roadside barn, which was traditionally used to advertise products to passing motorists.

Introduced in February 1994 and only available in North America during that year, the model is anticipated to be generally available from 1995 onwards.

Produced: 1994–
Height: 3-3/8 in./8½ cm
Versions: 1
Backstamp: O
Current value: £RRP ($RRP)

Blair Atholl

Scottish Collection (Limited Edition)

Blair Atholl, the ancient home of the Dukes of Atholl, is situated near Pitlochry in Tayside, Scotland.

Introduced in July 1989, Blair Atholl was limited to 3,000 pieces which were sold within three years.

Produced: 1989–92
Height: 5-1/8 in./
      13 cm
Versions: 1
Backstamp: J
Current value:
   £140–180
   ($350–400)

Bloemenmarkt

Netherlands Collection

Bloemenmarkt (The Flower Market) is one of the tallest models in the Netherlands Collection. The model is similar to De Zijdewever apart from the colouring.

Introduced in February 1991, Bloemenmarkt is still currently available.

Produced: 1991–
Height: 6¼ in./15½ cm
Versions: 1
Backstamp: L
Current value: £RRP ($RRP)

Bodiam

Historical Castles of England – South-East

Although Bodiam, in Sussex, was built in 1386 to discourage French raiders from sailing up the River Rother, the castle was never put to the test as a stronghold. Instead, from the late 1400s, the castle fell into neglect until 1829 when it was saved from demolition. The condition of the castle improved steadily with Lord Curzon finally restoring it when he took possession in 1917.

Introduced in July 1994, Bodiam is still current.

Produced: 1994–
Height: 3 in./7½ cm
Versions: 1
Backstamp: O
Current value: £RRP ($RRP)

Bow Cottage

English Collection – Midlands

Bow Cottage is situated in the Gloucestershire village of Badminton. The cottage, which was designed by Thomas Wright during the 1750s, has rendered stone walls which gently curve in a bow toward each end.

Introduced in February 1992, the model is still current, although it is due to be retired in March 1995.

Produced: 1992–95
Height: 3½ in./8½ cm
Versions: 1
Backstamp: M
Current value: £RRP ($RRP)

B

Bramble Cottage

English Collection – Midlands

Bramble Cottage can be found in a tiny village in Berkshire, where a number of similar cottages can be found set around the village green and pond. All of the cottages were built during the 16th and 17th centuries.

Introduced in February 1990, Bramble Cottage is still currently available, although it is due to be retired in March 1995.

Produced: 1990–95
Height: 3¼ in./8 cm
Versions: 1
Backstamp: K
Current value: £RRP ($RRP)

De Branderij

Netherlands Collection

As gin had become a very popular drink towards the end of the 17th century, De Branderij (The Distillery) is the type of house that a distiller would have been able to afford.

Introduced in February 1991, De Branderij is similar in appearance to De Wolhandelaar apart from the colouring; the model is still currently available.

Produced: 1991–
Height: 5¼ in./13½ cm
Versions: 1
Backstamp: L
Current value: £RRP ($RRP)

Brecon Bach

Welsh Collection

Brecon Bach can be found close to Pen-y-Fan, which at 2,906 feet is the highest peak in the Brecon Beacons. Typical of the small farmhouses in this region of Wales, Brecon Bach is constructed of stone and slate.

Introduced in February 1986, Brecon Bach was retired in July 1993.

Produced: 1986–93
Height: 3 in./7½ cm
Versions: 1
Backstamp: F
Current value: £40–50 ($70–90)

Bredon House

English Collection – Midlands

Located close to Stratford-upon-Avon, Bredon House was named after a well-known local hill which, in early days, was believed to be a magic or mystical place. Using a variety of materials, the house has a distinctive 'magpie' style.

Introduced in September 1988, the model was retired in December 1990.

Produced: 1988–90
Height: 4¼ in./11 cm
Versions: 1
Backstamp: H
Current value: £90–110 ($150–175)

B

The Briary

English Collection – South-West

The Briary is one of the Gothic buildings which can be found at Stourhead in Wiltshire.

Introduced in February 1989, The Briary is still current.

Produced: 1989–
Height: 2¾ in./7 cm
Versions: 1
Backstamp: J
Current value: £RRP ($RRP)

Bridge House

Dealer Sign

Introduced in September 1982 as a promotional 'dealer sign' for use by Lilliput Lane retailers, the inscription at the foot of the bridge reads:

BRIDGE HOUSE

LILLIPUT LANE

However, in November 1982 (within two months of being introduced), the model was replaced by a new flat-back version for use by retailers, and was also modified and introduced into the general range (see later).

Produced: 1982
Height: 2½ in./7 cm
Versions: 1
Backstamp: None used
Current value: £750–850 ($1,200–1,500)

Bridge House

*Dealer Sign
(Flat-Back)*

The second promotional 'dealer sign' was introduced in November 1982. Intended to stand flat against a wall, on the front was the wording:

THE LILLIPUT LANE COLLECTION

MADE IN THE BORDERS

In August 1983, the model was restyled when it was made thinner and the wording changed to:

THE LILLIPUT LANE COLLECTION

MADE IN ENGLAND

Production of the model was discontinued in December 1984.

Produced: 1982–84
Height: 4 in./10¼ cm
Versions: 2
Backstamp: None used
Current value:
   Version 1 – £450–550 ($750–1,000)
   Version 2 – £300–350 ($600–750)

Bridge House

English Collection – Northern

Bridge House spans Stock Ghyll in Ambleside, Cumbria. Now owned by The National Trust, Bridge House was thought to have been built originally as a summer-house or apple store.

Introduced in November 1982, the model was derived from the promotional 'dealer sign' used by Lilliput Lane retailers. The inscription at the foot of the bridge reads:

BRIDGE HOUSE

The model was retired in December 1990.

Produced: 1982–90
Height: 2½ in./7 cm
Versions: 1
Backstamp: None used
Current value: £20–30 ($50–75)

Bridge House 1991

English Collection – Northern

Slightly larger and more refined than the original model, Bridge House 1991 was introduced in February 1991. On the side of the wall is the inscription:

BRIDGE HOUSE 1991

The model is still currently available.

Produced: 1991–
Height: 3 in./7½ cm
Versions: 1
Backstamp: None used
Current value: £RRP ($RRP)

B

Bridle Way

Collectors Club

Bridle Way publicised the craft of thatching and featured a thatcher at work on the roof.

Introduced in March 1990, Bridle Way was only available to members of the Lilliput Lane Collectors Club for the 12-month period until February 1991; the model was never generally available.

Produced: 1990–91
Height: 3¾ in./9½ cm
Versions: 1
Backstamp: K
Current value: £130–160
    ($150–200)

Bro Dawel

Welsh Collection

Bro Dawel is typical of the cob and thatch cottages once found in Dyfed in the west of Wales; unfortunately, only a few of these cottages still exist in the less mountainous parts of the region.

Introduced in February 1991, Bro Dawel is still current.

Produced: 1991–
Height: 2 in./5 cm
Versions: 1
Backstamp: L
Current value: £RRP ($RRP)

Brockbank

English Collection – South-East

Originally a timber-framed, jettied building from the 17th century, in later times Brockbank has had walls built outside the timber frame on the ground floor, and then tiles hung to provide extra weather protection on the upper floors.

Introduced in February 1988, the model was retired in December 1993.

Produced: 1988–93
Height: 3½ in./8½ cm
Versions: 1
Backstamp: H
Current value: £30–40 ($80–100)

Brontë Parsonage

English Collection – Northern

Standing high on the moors at Haworth, Yorkshire, this Georgian house was once the home of the Brontë family.

Introduced in July 1985, the model was originally known as The Parsonage. Early production pieces had window frames which were very thin and almost non-existent, whereas on pieces produced after a few months the window frames were noticeably thicker.

Brontë Parsonage was retired in December 1987.

Produced: 1985–87
Height: 3¾ in./9½ cm
Versions: 2
Backstamp: E
Current value:
   Version 1 – £150–175
     ($250–300)
   Version 2 – £80–100
     ($150–200)

Der Bücherwurm

German Collection

Der Bücherwurm (The Bookworm) is typical of the medieval buildings found in the ancient university town of Tübingen. Situated on the River Neckar in the Baden-Württemberg region of Germany, Tübingen, which was founded in 1477, is full of bustling, narrow streets running between attractive medieval buildings.

Introduced in February 1992, Der Bücherwurm is still current.

Produced: 1992–
Height: 4¼ in./11 cm
Versions: 1
Backstamp: M
Current value: £RRP ($RRP)

Burns Cottage, Alloway

Scottish Collection

This gardener's cottage at Alloway, 2 miles south of Ayr in Scotland, was the birthplace of Robert Burns. Born on 25 January 1759, Burns is regarded as Scotland's greatest poet, and each year – on Burns Night – his birth date is celebrated by Scots throughout the world. Burns Cottage is now a museum.

Introduced in February 1985, Burns Cottage was retired in December 1988.

Produced: 1985–88
Height: 2 in./5 cm
Versions: 1
Backstamp: E
Current value: £60–80 ($100–125)

Burnside

*English Collection –
Northern*

When Burnside was first introduced in November 1982 it was also known as Burnside Cottage. However, after being restyled in 1983, when the model was made larger and the door of the shed was coloured similar to the roof, it was also known as Burnside House.

In July 1985, Burnside was retired.

Produced: 1982–85
Height: 3¼ in./8 cm; version 1 smaller
Versions: 2
Backstamp: A, C
Current value:
   Version 1 – £475–550 ($700–900)
   Version 2 – £250–300 ($400–500)

Buster

Miscellaneous

Little is known about the set of five clowns which were produced between 1983 and 1984.

Buster has recorded sales of less than 100 pieces.

Produced: 1983–84
Height: 4–5 in./10–12½ cm
Versions: 1
Backstamp: A
Current value: £550–650 ($1,500+)

Buttercup Cottage

English Collection – Midlands

Buttercup Cottage, which can be found in Gloucestershire, is a simple cruck-framed cottage built in the mid-1700s.

Introduced in February 1990, the cottage had a short production run and was retired in December 1992.

Produced: 1990–92
Height: 2¾ in./7 cm
Versions: 1
Backstamp: K
Current value: £30–35 ($50–75)

Butterwick

English Collection – South-West

Butterwick is reminiscent of the type of thatched cottage that would have been built around 1830 in the North Devon and Somerset areas, when picturesque styles based on the vernacular were very popular.

Introduced in February 1989, the model is still current.

Produced: 1989–
Height: 2¾ in./7 cm
Versions: 1
Backstamp: J
Current value: £RRP ($RRP)

La Cabane du Gardian

French Collection

La Cabane du Gardian (The Horsekeeper's Hut) is found in the wide, flat land of the Camargue in the south of France. The Camargue is famous for its colonies of flamingoes and its wild horses.

Introduced in September 1990, this is the smallest model in the French Collection and it is still current.

Produced: 1990–
Height: 2 in./5 cm
Versions: 1
Backstamp: K
Current value: £RRP ($RRP)

Camomile Lawn

English Collection – South-East

Therfield, winner on many occasions of the title Best Kept Village in Hertfordshire, was once owned by Henry VIII, who in 1541 presented the village to Catherine Howard.

Camomile Lawn, a 17th century house close to Therfield, is a half-timbered building with white plaster infill, oak-framed leaded windows and thatched roof.

Introduced in February 1994, the model is still current.

Produced: 1994–
Height: 3¼ in./8 cm
Versions: 1
Backstamp: O
Current value: £RRP ($RRP)

Cape Cod Cottage

American Collection – 1st Series

Cape Cod Cottage is a clapboard building with a tiled roof, typical of the buildings in the New England coastal areas of the USA.

Introduced in October 1984, the cottage was retired a year later in October 1985; only 225 pieces were produced.

Produced: 1984–85
Height: 2½ in./6½ cm
Versions: 1
Backstamp: D
Current value: £375–400
  ($550–650)

Carrick House

Scottish Collection

Carrick House is typical of the many houses to be found in the Lowlands of Scotland, south of Edinburgh. Originally the properties would have been built to house the workers on the laird's estate.

Introduced in July 1989, the model is still currently available.

Produced: 1989–
Height: 2½ in./6½ cm
Versions: 1
Backstamp: J
Current value: £RRP ($RRP)

Castell Coch

Historical Castles of England – Welsh

Castell Coch (the 'Red Castle') is 5 miles north-west of Cardiff, overlooking the River Taff. Just over 100 years old, Castell Coch was built on the site of a ruined medieval castle. In 1865, Lord Bute (the Third Marquess of Bute) asked the architect William Burges to rebuild the castle. Burges designed the castle as he imagined it would have been, but Burges was never to see his work, because he died in 1881, ten years before the building was completed.

Introduced in July 1994, Castell Coch is still currently available.

Produced: 1994–
Height: 5½ in./14 cm
Versions: 1
Backstamp: O
Current value: £RRP ($RRP)

Cats Coombe Cottage

English Collection – South-West

Cats Coombe Cottage can be found in 'Thomas Hardy country' near Wool in Dorset. Hardy used his native county as the location for most of his novels.

Cats Coombe Cottage is an example of the early 'natural' cottage design, where natural materials were used in the construction. Introduced in February 1993, this model is still current.

Produced: 1993–
Height: 2¾ in./7 cm
Versions: 1
Backstamp: N
Current value: £RRP ($RRP)

C

Castle Street

English Collection – Northern

Castle Street is typical of an area where development has centred around a Pele tower or castle. In the Middle Ages, the wooden buildings would have been ransacked and burnt by invaders, but other dwellings would then have been built in the safety and security of the tower.

Introduced in November 1982, within a few months Castle Street was restyled: the rock base at the rear was filled in and the company name added; the name was embossed instead of engraved; and the rock base to the left of the entrance, which was originally filled in, was cut away so that the moat was more easily seen. However, although the restyling took place in December 1983, the original mould was still used until Autumn 1984. Production of Castle Street was halted for 6 months in 1984, and in December 1986 the model was retired.

Produced: 1982–86
Height: 5½ in./14 cm
Versions: 2
Backstamp: C, D
Current value:
   Version 1 – £325–350 ($500–750)
   Version 2 – £250–275 ($350–450)

Adobe Church

*From the American Collection – 1st Series,
produced 1984–85*

Bermuda Cottage

*An exclusive model, produced 1985–91 in three
colourways, for The Britannia, a Bermudan company*

Country Church

From the American Collection – 1st Series,
produced 1984–85 in two colourways

Covered Memories

From the American Landmarks collection, produced 1990–93

Cawdor Castle

Scottish Collection (Limited Edition)

Cawdor Castle, near Inverness, is well known as the castle in Shakespeare's play *Macbeth*. In its 600-year history, Cawdor has been extended and modified a number of times. Originally built and owned by the Cawdor family, in 1510 it passed into the ownership of the Campbells.

Introduced in February 1990, Cawdor Castle, which was limited to 3,000 pieces, was sold out within four years.

Produced: 1990–93
Height: 6 in./15 cm
Versions: 1
Backstamp: K
Current value: £200–225 ($300–350)

Chantry Chapel

Exclusive

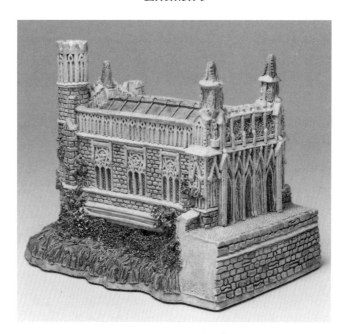

Chantry Chapel was commissioned in 1988 by an English company, Peter Jones China, and was only available through their stores.

Introduced in November 1988, the model was retired in March 1991.

Produced: 1988–91
Height: 4¼ in./10½ cm
Versions: 1
Backstamp: H
Current value: £130–150 ($200–250)

Chatsworth View

English Collection – Northern

Close to Chatsworth House (the home of the Duke of Devonshire), at Edensor in Derbyshire, is Chatsworth View. Built in the 19th century, Chatsworth View is an attractive lodge house. Timber framed on stone, one of its major features is its scalloped slate roof and stone chimneys.

Introduced in July 1991, this model is still current.

Produced: 1991–
Height: 5 in./12½ cm
Versions: 1
Backstamp: L
Current value: £RRP ($RRP)

C

La Chaumiere du Verger

French Collection

La Chaumiere du Verger (Orchard Cottage) is a typical close-studded timber-framed farmhouse which can be found on the Normandy coast. Roofed with local thatch, wild irises are planted in a clay ridge to bind the individual reeds together.

Introduced in September 1990, the model is still currently available.

Produced: 1990–
Height: 3¼ in./8½ cm

Versions: 1
Backstamp: K
Current value: £RRP ($RRP)

Cherry Cottage

English Collection – South-East

Cherry Cottage is typical of the colour washed plaster, traditionally white, pink or buff, found on many of the buildings in Suffolk. Introduced in July 1990, this model is still current.

Produced: 1990–
Height: 2¾ in./7 cm
Versions: 1
Backstamp: K
Current value: £RRP ($RRP)

Chestnut Cottage

Christmas Collection

Chestnut Cottage is situated close to the village of Bibury in Gloucestershire.

Introduced in March 1992, a new, effective technique of 'icing sugar' snow was used. The model is still current.

Produced: 1992–
Height: 2-3/8 in./6 cm
Versions: 1
Backstamp: M
Current value: £RRP ($RRP)

Chiltern Mill

English Collection – Midlands

Chiltern Mill is a 17th-century post mill, which was pivoted on sunken poles and used for milling wheat and barley.

Introduced in July 1989, initially Chiltern Mill was exclusive to H Samuel, the UK chain of jewellery stores. However, the model was then incorporated into the general range and is still current, although it is due to be retired in March 1995.

Produced: 1989–95
Height: 6¾ in./16½ cm
Versions: 1
Backstamp: J
Current value: £RRP ($RRP)

Chine Cot
English Collection – South-East

Chine Cot is typical of the sandstone cottages which can be found on the Isle of Wight.

Introduced in July 1987, the cottage was restyled in December 1989, when four windows were removed and bricked up (although it is still noticeable that the windows were originally there), and the doors became solid (originally the front and back doors had 'glass effect' panes). The colouring used on the steps at the front of the cottage and on the footpath was also changed, from grey (on the original version) to cream (on the second version). The model is still current.

Produced: 1987–
Height: 2½ in./6½ cm
Versions: 2
Backstamp: J
Current value:
 Version 1 – £25–35 ($50–70)
 Version 2 – £RRP ($RRP)

Front view:
version 1 (left);
version 2 (right)

Side view:
version 1 (left);
version 2 (right)

The Chocolate House

English Collection – Northern

The Chocolate House is based upon a stone cottage which can be found just off the Market Place in Kendal, Cumbria. Built in 1630, the building has been used for a variety of purposes, but today it is the only contemporary chocolate house in England, evoking memories of the mid-1600s when the first chocolate shop opened in England, and solid chocolate for making the drink cost between 10 and 15 shillings per pound.

Introduced in July 1992, the model is still currently available.

Produced: 1992–
Height: 4½ in./11½ cm
Versions: 1
Backstamp: M
Current value: £RRP ($RRP)

C

Circular Cottage
Blaise Hamlet Collection

All of the cottages from Blaise Hamlet, near Bristol, portrayed by Lilliput Lane, were designed by the architects John Nash and George Repton, and were built around 1810.

Circular Cottage is probably the most unusual design in Blaise Hamlet, with its sweeping semi-circular feature, a Dorset-type thatch and lean-to's running down from the main eaves.

Introduced in February 1989, Circular Cottage was retired in December 1993.

Produced: 1989–93
Height: 4½ in./11½ cm
Versions: 1
Backstamp: J
Current value: £50–60 ($150–175)

Circular Cottage
Classics Collection

All of the nine miniature cottages in the Classics Collection are based upon the buildings in the village of Blaise Hamlet, near Bristol, which has already provided the subjects for the Blaise Hamlet Collection. Circular Cottage is an unusual design with a sweeping semi-circular feature.

Introduced in February 1993, the model is still current, although it is due to be retired in March 1995.

Produced: 1993–95
Height: 2-3/8 in./6 cm
Versions: 1
Backstamp: N
Current value: £RRP ($RRP)

Clare Cottage

English Collection — South-East

Based upon the thatched cottages to be found in the village of Clare in Suffolk, Clare Cottage is modelled upon a building which dates from 1658. The cottage has examples on its front and gable ends of the decorated relief plaster work known as pargeting. First used in Elizabethan times, pargeting is unique to this area of England.

Introduced in February 1985, Clare Cottage was retired in July 1993.

Produced: 1985–93
Height: 3 in./7½ cm
Versions: 1
Backstamp: E
Current value: £20–25 ($40–50)

C

Clarence

Miscellaneous

As with Alphonse, Buster, Danny and Emile (the other models in this five-model series of clowns), little is known about Clarence.

Introduced in 1983, the model was retired in 1984. Sales are believed to have been very low, with possibly less than 100 pieces being sold.

Produced: 1983–84
Height: 4–5 in./10–12½ cm
Versions: 1
Backstamp: A
Current value: £550–650 ($1,500+)

Claypotts Castle
Scottish Collection

Claypotts Castle, which is now a well-preserved ruin, stands overlooking the Tay, near Dundee. Built in 1588, the castle was once the home of James Graham of Claverhouse.

Introduced in July 1989, the model is still current.

Produced: 1989–
Height: 5-1/8 in./13 cm
Versions: 1
Backstamp: J
Current value: £RRP ($RRP)

Cley-next-the-Sea
English Collection – South-East

This 18th-century windmill, which overlooks Blakeney harbour in Norfolk, is a well-known coastal landmark.

Introduced in July 1992, this model was limited to 3,000 pieces; in the UK it was only available to members of the Lilliput Lane Collectors Club. Cley-next-the-Sea is believed to be close to being fully subscribed.

Produced: 1992–
Height: 8½ in./22 cm
Versions: 1
Backstamp: M
Current value: £RRP ($RRP)

Cliburn School

Miscellaneous

One of the three rarest Lilliput Lane cottages (the others being Drapers and Old Mill), Cliburn School was introduced in June 1983. It is believed that the model was produced and sold to raise funds for the School, and was available for sale to all those who attended the School. The model carried its own special label which read:

> LILLIPUT LANE
> CLIBURN SCHOOL
> SPECIAL EDITION 1860–83
> A GENUINE LILLIPUT
> LANE PRODUCT.

Only 64 pieces were produced and the model was retired in February 1984, the mould then being used for Old School House.

Produced: 1983–84
Height: 2½ in./6½ cm
Versions: 1
Backstamp: A
Current value: £2,500–3,000 ($5,000–7,000)

Clockmaker's Cottage

Exclusive

Clockmaker's Cottage was only available through H Samuel (a chain of jewellery stores) in the UK, and through Peoples Jewellers in Canada.

Introduced in October 1987, the model was retired in December 1990.

Produced: 1987–90
Height: 4 in./10 cm
Versions: 1
Backstamp: G
Current value: £140–160 ($200–250)

Clover Cottage

English Collection – South-West

Clover Cottage, a half-hip shaped thatch, is typical of many cottages to be found in Devon. The walls are of cob – a mixture of mud, straw and cow dung – which is then lime-washed.

Introduced in July 1987, the model was retired in July 1994.

Produced: 1987–94
Height: 2 in./5 cm
Versions: 1
Backstamp: G
Current value: £20–25 ($30–40)

Coach House

English Collection – South-East

Introduced in September 1982, Coach House was soon remodelled in December 1982, when the crosses beneath the eaves were removed. Major changes were then made to the model in August 1983: chimneys were remodelled; windows were removed; and the lattice work across the front of the building was changed from a criss-cross style to a distinctive 'V'-shape style.

Coach House was retired in July 1985.

Produced: 1982–85
Height: 4 in./10 cm
Versions: 3
Backstamp: A, C
Current value:
    Version 1 – £750–800
      ($1,800–2,200)
    Version 2 – £550–600
      ($1,300–1,500)
    Version 3 – £450–500
      ($1,000–1,250)

Cobblers Cottage

English Collection — Midlands

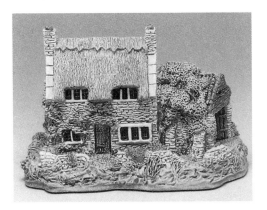

Cobblers Cottage is typical of the cottages to be found in Northamptonshire. Built of mellow Cotswold limestone and thatched with reeds, the cottage may well have been occupied by a shoemaker in an area long famed for its leatherwork.

Introduced in February 1986, Cobblers Cottage was retired in July 1994.

Produced: 1986–94
Height: 2½ in./6½ cm
Versions: 1
Backstamp: F
Current value: £20–25 ($50–60)

Convent in the Woods

English Collection — South-West

C

Based upon a cottage in the grounds of Stourhead, near Mere, in Wiltshire, Convent in the Woods is typical of the many unusual buildings which were designed to enhance the large parks and gardens of the 18th century. With its gardens, lakes and temples, Stourhead is regarded as one of the finest landscape designs of that time.

Introduced in July 1990, Convent in the Woods was retired in July 1994.

Produced: 1990–94
Height: 4½ in./ 11½ cm
Versions: 1
Backstamp: K
Current value: £75–85 ($140–180)

Coopers

English Collection – South-East

Typical of the cottages to be found in the forested areas of West Sussex, Coopers is built of local flint with a curved clay tile roof.

Introduced in February 1983, Coopers was restyled in October 1983, when it was reduced in size by about a quarter, and the appearance of the base became more pitted.

Coopers was retired in March 1986.

Produced: 1983–86
Height: 2¾ in./7 cm; version 1 larger
Versions: 2
Backstamp: A, C
Current value:
   Version 1 – £250–300 ($400–500)
   Version 2 – £150–200 ($225–300)

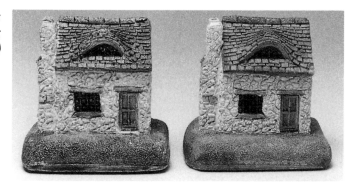

Front view: version 2 (left); version 1 (right)

Back view: version 2 (left); version 1 (right)

Cosy Corner

Collectors Club

Cosy Corner showed a tranquil garden hideaway with a wooden bench recessed in a stone wall and a cat sleeping peacefully upon the bench.

Introduced in March 1990, Cosy Corner was a free gift for members who joined the Collectors Club during the 12 months from March 1990 to February 1991, at which time it was retired.

Produced: 1990–91
Height: 2¾ in./7 cm
Versions: 1
Backstamp: K
Current value: £60–80 ($75–100)

Cotman Cottage

Anniversary

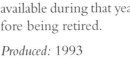

Situated in the north-west corner of Suffolk, Cotman Cottage dates from the early 18th century. Heavily timber framed, the walls have been plastered and then lime-washed.

Introduced in February 1993, as with all Anniversary models Cotman Cottage was only available during that year before being retired.

Produced: 1993
Height: 4 in./10 cm
Versions: 1
Backstamp: N
Current value: £55–65 ($175–200)

Counting House Corner

Miscellaneous

Counting House Corner was based upon the earlyVictorian-style buildings reminiscent of Dickensian London. Produced to commemorate Lilliput Group plc becoming a publicly quoted company, the production run was limited to 3,093, which was the level of the Financial Times Stock Exchange 100 Index at the close of business on the first day that Lilliput Group plc shares were traded (25 November 1993).

Only UK members of the Lilliput Lane Collectors Club were allowed to apply for the model, and from the 10,270 member applications, 3,093 lucky names were randomly drawn. A further 300 to 500 pieces were also mounted on plinths and distributed to Lilliput Group shareholders.

Produced: 1993
Height: 4½ in./11½ cm
Versions: 1

Backstamp: N
Current value:
  Mounted – £350+ ($675–750)
  Unmounted – £250+ ($600–650)

Country Church

American Collection – 1st Series

Introduced in October 1984, Country Church was soon undergoing colour changes. Initial production pieces had a brown building, white windows, white bell tower, brown door and brown steps. The colours were then changed to white building, brown windows, brown bell tower and white door.

Of the 500 pieces produced, the majority were in the second colourway; pieces in the original colourway are quite rare. Country Church was retired in October 1985.

Produced: 1984–85
Height: 2¾ in./7 cm
Versions: 2
Backstamp: D
Current value:
    Version 1 – £500–600 ($1,000+)
    Version 2 – £300–350 ($500+)

Version 1

Version 2

Country Church

American Landmarks

This typical American church, set in the heart of the countryside, recalls memories of summer with the roses climbing up the red building towards the steeple.

Introduced in June 1989, Country Church was retired in December 1992.

Produced: 1989–92
Height: 4 in./10 cm
Versions: 1
Backstamp: J
Current value: £60–70
   ($125–150)

Countryside Barn

American Landmarks

This traditional American wooden barn was introduced in June 1989, and was retired in December 1992.

Produced: 1989–92
Height: 3½ in./9 cm
Versions: 1
Backstamp: J
Current value: £60–70
   ($125–150)

Covered Bridge

American Collection – 1st Series

Introduced in October 1984, Covered Bridge was only available for 12 months. As with the other models in the American Collection, Covered Bridge was not very popular, and although the actual number of pieces produced is not known, it is believed that the model is quite rare. Covered Bridge was retired in October 1985.

Produced: 1984–85
Height: 2½ in./6½ cm
Versions: 1
Backstamp: D
Current value: £600–700
　　($900–1,200)

C

Covered Memories

American Landmarks

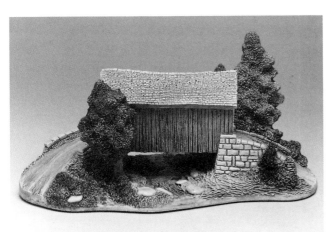

Based upon the well-known, historic wooden covered bridge (which is now a protected building in the USA), this model was introduced in March 1990, and was retired in December 1993.

Produced: 1990–93
Height: 3½ in./9 cm
Versions: 1
Backstamp: K
Current value: £75–80 ($150–200)

Craigievar Castle
Scottish Collection

Cranberry Cottage
Christmas Collection

From Minchinhampton Common (between Stroud and Cirencester), Cranberry Cottage can be seen in one of the villages clinging to the slopes of the Cotswolds. Built from golden-coloured stone and with a thatched roof, the cottage enjoys spectacular views across the surrounding countryside. Introduced in February 1992, Cranberry Cottage is still currently available.

Craigievar Castle, situated about 30 miles west of Aberdeen, is a small, high-turreted, fairy-tale castle practically unchanged since it was completed in 1626. Built by the Forbes family, the walls are harled in the distinct and unusual colour of pale apricot which adds to the castle's fairy-tale appearance.

Introduced in July 1989, the model was retired in December 1991.

Produced: 1992–
Height: 2-3/8 in./6 cm
Versions: 1
Backstamp: M
Current value: £RRP ($RRP)

Produced: 1989–91
Height: 6¾ in./17 cm
Versions: 1
Backstamp: J
Current value: £100–130 ($200–250)

Creel Cottage
English Collection – South-West

Based upon a similar building in Polperro, Cornwall, this granite-built, white-washed fisherman's cottage has

Crendon Manor

Collectors Club
(Limited Edition)

Crendon Manor was based upon a late 16th/early 17th-century building in Long Crendon, Buckinghamshire.

Introduced in November 1986, Crendon Manor had the distinction of not only being the first model to be offered exclusively to Lilliput Lane Collectors Club members (who numbered around 3,500 at that time), it was also limited to 1,500 pieces. Each piece was individually numbered and carried a distinctive label in gold lettering.

Crendon Manor was retired in February 1989.

been tile-hung on the corner facing the prevailing wind to give added protection against the severe Atlantic weather.

Introduced in July 1994, Creel Cottage is still current.

Produced: 1994–
Height: 2½ in./6 cm
Versions: 1
Backstamp: O
Current value: £RRP
    ($RRP)

Produced: 1986–89
Height: 4½ in./11½ cm
Versions: 1
Backstamp: F
Current value: £300–400 ($900–1,200)

C

Crendon Manor: the very first model to be offered exclusively to the members of the Collectors Club, as well as being a limited edition of 1,500 pieces

The Croft/ Crofter's Cottage

Scottish Collection

Typical of the stone cottages found in the Highlands and Islands region of Scotland, Crofter's Cottage was introduced in September 1982.

In 1983 it was renamed The Croft, but other than the backstamp changing from A to C, no restyling took place until July 1984, when chimney pots were removed and sheep were added.

The Croft was retired in December 1991.

Produced: 1982–91
Height: 2¼ in./5¾ cm
Versions: 3
Backstamp: A, C, D
Current value:
  Version 1 – £500–600 ($1,000–1,250)
  Version 2 – £400–500 ($800–1,000)
  Version 3 – £50–60 ($100–125)

Front view: version 1 (left); version 3 (right)

Side view: version 1 (left); version 3 (right)

Back view: version 1 (left); version 3 (right)

Crown Inn

English Collection – South-East

Situated in Chiddingfold, Surrey, the Crown Inn is constructed of timber framing in-filled with plaster and brick. The main roof, pent roofs and gable end are covered with clay tiles.

Introduced in September 1988, the model was retired in July 1992.

Produced: 1988–92
Height: 4½ in./11½ cm
Versions: 1
Backstamp: H
Current value: £70–80
  ($125–150)

C

Culloden Cottage

Scottish Collection

In the windswept north-east corner of Scotland many cottages similar to Culloden Cottage can be found. Built of thick stone, the single-storey cottage provides protection from the North Sea weather.

Introduced in July 1989, the model is still currently available.

Produced: 1989–
Height: 2-3/8 in./6 cm
Versions: 1
Backstamp: J
Current value: £RRP ($RRP)

Culross House

Scottish Collection

With its crow-stepped gables, pantile roofs, outside stairways and decorative stone lintels, Culross House is typical of Scottish vernacular architecture.

Introduced in February 1992, Culross House is still current.

Produced: 1992–
Height: 3¾ in./9½ cm
Versions: 1
Backstamp: M
Current value: £RRP ($RRP)

Curlew Cottage

Collectors Club

Curlew Cottage was based upon a South Yorkshire dwelling which was built in 1885 by a local shepherd.

Introduced in March 1993, Curlew Cottage was offered at a preferential price to Club members who enrolled a friend; the cottage was not obtainable through retailers.

Curlew Cottage was retired in February 1994.

Produced: 1993–94
Height: 2¾ in./7 cm
Versions: 1
Backstamp: N
Current value: £50–60 ($100–125)

Daisy Cottage

English Collection – South-East

Daisy Cottage is based upon the 17th-century single-storey timber-framed thatched cottages which were abundant in Hertfordshire. Introduced in February 1991, this model is still current.

Produced: 1991–
Height: 2 in./5 cm
Versions: 1
Backstamp: L
Current value: £RRP ($RRP)

Dale Farm

English Collection – Northern

Introduced in September 1982, Dale Farm was restyled in September 1983 when a window at the rear of the main building (under the L-shaped left eave) was removed; a window at the rear of the middle section of the building (under the horizontal eave) was removed; and a bush was added at the front, left side of the building. It would also appear there were colour changes at some time (see below), as well as differences in the size of the base. Dale Farm was retired in December 1986.

Produced: 1982–86
Height: 2½ in./6 cm
Versions: 2
Backstamp: A, C
Current value:
    Version 1 – £650–750 ($1,200–1,500)
    Version 2 – £350–500 ($750–1,000)

Dale Farm: two pieces which show the variation in the colouring

Dale Head

English Collection – Northern

Built from local York stone (which is a warm, yellow sandstone), Dale Farm is typical of the farms and buildings to be found in Yorkshire.

Introduced in February 1986, Dale Farm was retired in December 1988.

Produced: 1986–88
Height: 2¾ in./7 cm
Versions: 1
Backstamp: F
Current value: £60–80
     ($125–150)

Dale House

English Collection – Northern

The original version of Dale House, which was introduced in September 1982, was sculpted by David Tate, the founder of Lilliput Lane.

In September 1983 it was remodelled in a more detailed style: the windows and doorways were larger and better proportioned; the stairway was wider and had fewer steps; at the top of the steps a window was added parallel to the door; the ivy/foliage at the front of the building was extended up to the top of the first floor window; and more foliage was added at the rear of the building. As well as these changes, the restyled version was also a third larger in size than the original. Dale House was retired in December 1986.

Produced: 1982–86
Height: 2 in./5 cm; version 1 smaller
Versions: 2
Backstamp: A, C
Current value:
   Version 1 – £650–750 ($1,200–1,500)
   Version 2 – £350–500 ($750–1,000)

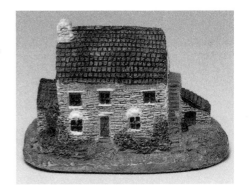

Danny

Miscellaneous

Danny, another of the clowns, was introduced in 1983. Although only available for one year, Danny was remodelled. Originally wearing a red jacket and leaning forwards with his hands on his stomach (this model carried backstamp A), Danny was remodelled with a beige jacket, a large yellow and blue tie, and leaning backwards with his hands on his stomach (this model carried backstamp C).

Danny was retired in 1984. Recorded sales of the original version are less than 100 pieces, and even though more pieces were made of the re-styled version, it is still rare.

Produced: 1983–84
Height: 5–6 in./12½–15 cm
Versions: 2
Backstamp: A, C
Current value: Version 1 – £800–900 ($2,500+)
　　Version 2 – £550–650 ($1,500+)

Deer Park Hall

Christmas Specials

Standing high on the East Sussex Downs, Deer Park Hall has a sturdy oak frame in-filled with herring-bone brickwork.

Introduced in September 1988, this was the first Christmas model to be produced; it was retired in February 1989.

Produced: 1988–89
Height: 5¼ in./13 cm
Versions: 1
Backstamp: H
Current value: £140–170 ($225–300)

D

Derwent-le-Dale

English Collection – Northern

An example of 18th century cottage building, Derwent-le-Dale, is a thatched limestone cottage situated on a tributary of the River Derwent.

Introduced in July 1992, Derwent-le-Dale is still current.

Produced: 1992–
Height: 2¾ in./7 cm
Versions: 1
Backstamp: M
Current value: £RRP ($RRP)

Dial Cottage

English Collection – South-West

Initially one of the nine cottages which made up the Blaise Hamlet Collection, in 1994 Dial Cottage and the other five Blaise Hamlet cottages still current at that time were transferred to the English Collection – South-West.

Introduced in February 1990, Dial Cottage is unique amongst the buildings in Blaise Hamlet, near Bristol, in that it is the only one where brick has been conspicuously used in the main wall.

Dial Cottage is due to be retired in March 1995.

Produced: 1990–95
Height: 4½ in./11½ cm
Versions: 1
Backstamp: K
Current value: £RRP ($RRP)

Dial Cottage

Classics Collection

Taking its name from the focal point of the village green – a water pump and sun dial – Dial Cottage, in Blaise Hamlet, near Bristol, was designed by the architects John Nash and George Repton.

Introduced in February 1993 as part of the miniature Classics Collection, Dial Cottage is due to be retired in March 1995.

Produced: 1993–95
Height: 2-3/8 in./6 cm
Versions: 1
Backstamp: N
Current value: £RRP ($RRP)

De Diamantair

Netherlands Collection

This large house shows the wealth gained from one of Amsterdam's most famous industries – diamonds. The Amsterdam diamond industry has always been dominated by the city's Jewish residents: in 1748 about 600 Jewish families were engaged in the trade, but after 1870 when diamonds were being shipped in from South Africa the number increased to over 3,000.

Introduced in February 1991, De Diamantair (The Diamond Merchant), is similar to Aan de Amstel apart from the colouring, and is still current.

D

Produced: 1991–
Height: 5¾ in./14½ cm
Versions: 1
Backstamp: L
Current value: £RRP ($RRP)

Diamond Cottage

Blaise Hamlet Collection

Situated in Blaise Hamlet, near Bristol, Diamond Cottage is a very geometric design, topped by tiles of stone and the type of chimney normally seen on old manor houses. The architects of Blaise Hamlet – John Nash and George Repton – had special bricks moulded for this and the other cottages in the village.

Introduced in February 1989, the model was retired in December 1993.

Produced: 1989–93
Height: 4¾ in./12 cm
Versions: 1
Backstamp: J
Current value: £50–55
($150–200)

Diamond Cottage

Classics Collection

Based upon the model previously issued as part of the Blaise Hamlet Collection, this Classics Collection cottage is a miniature version of its predecessor.

Introduced in February 1993, Diamond Cottage is due to be retired in March 1995.

Produced: 1993–95
Height: 2-3/8 in./6 cm
Versions: 1
Backstamp: N
Current value: £RRP ($RRP)

Donegal Cottage

Irish Collection

Donegal Cottage can be found on the north-west coast of Ireland. With walls built of stone, mud and limewash, and thatched with marram grass, the building stands up well to the fierce Atlantic weather. Introduced in July 1987, the model was retired in December 1992.

Produced: 1987–92
Height: 2 in./5 cm
Versions: 1
Backstamp: G
Current value: £25–30 ($45–55)

Double Cottage

English Collection – South-West

Originally designed by John Nash and George Repton, and built in 1810 by John Scandrett Harford, Double Cottage stands at one end of Blaise Hamlet village green. The largest of the buildings in the hamlet, the cottage was originally designed as two dwellings, and the different window styles show the two parts of the building.

Initially in the Blaise Hamlet Collection, in 1994 Double Cottage was transferred to the English Collection – South-West.

Introduced in February 1991, the model is still currently available.

Produced: 1991–
Height: 5 in./12½ cm
Versions: 1
Backstamp: L
Current value: £RRP ($RRP)

D

Double Cottage

Classics Collection

A miniature version based upon the larger model of Double Cottage, this cottage as well as the others in the Classics Collection can be seen at Blaise Hamlet, near Bristol.

Introduced in February 1993, the model is due to be retired in March 1995.

Produced: 1993–95
Height: 2-3/8 in./6 cm
Versions: 1
Backstamp: N
Current value: £RRP ($RRP)

Dove Cottage

English Collection – Northern

Renowned as the home of William Wordsworth, Dove Cottage at Grasmere in the Lake District was built in the early 17th century using local materials, including green Westmorland slate for the roof. The Cottage is now a museum dedicated to the life of Wordsworth, who wrote most of his major works whilst living there from 1799–1810.

Introduced in February 1983, Dove Cottage was restyled in September 1983, when the embossed name across the front of the base was removed.

Dove Cottage was retired in December 1988.

Produced: 1983–88
Height: 2-3/8 in./6 cm
Versions: 2
Backstamp: A, C
Current value:
    Version 1 – £550–600 ($1,200–1,400)
    Version 2 – £50–60 ($85–100)

Front view: version 1 (left); version 2 (right)

Craigievar Castle

From the Scottish Collection, produced 1989–91

Dale Farm (left) and Dale House (right)

Both from the English Collection – Northern, produced 1982–86

Clowns

From left to right: (above) Danny (bending backwards), Danny (bending forwards), and Clarence; (below) Emile (first version), Buster and Alphonse

Dovecot

Collectors Club

Dovecot was the joining gift for members of the Collectors Club from March 1989 to February 1990 (the fourth year of the Club). Based upon a building in the south-west of England, Dovecot was modelled complete with white doves.

Produced: 1989–90
Height: 3 in./7½ cm
Versions: 1
Backstamp: J
Current value: £60–80 ($95–125)

Dovetails

English Collection – Northern

Based upon a building in the centre of Ilkley, in Yorkshire, Dovetails was originally a school. Built in 1635, the building was used as a school until 1869, when it was sold to a cabinetmaker. Having been used for a variety of purposes since the cabinetmaker left the building, it is today an antique shop.

Introduced in July 1991, Dovetails is still currently available.

Produced: 1991–
Height: 3¼ in./8 cm
Versions: 1
Backstamp: L
Current value: £RRP ($RRP)

D

Drapers

English Collection – Midlands

One of the rarest models produced by Lilliput Lane, Drapers was introduced in September 1982. On the original version, the base and the building were in a beige/sandy colour, with windows trimmed in red and a red roof.

Even though the cottage was only produced for a short time, there was a colour change at some point, when the building became an overall beige.

Only 360 pieces had been produced when Drapers was retired in July 1983.

Produced: 1982–83
Height: 2¾ in./7 cm
Versions: 2

Backstamp: A
Current value:
Version 1 – £1,300–1,500 ($2,750–3,000)
Version 2 – £1,000–1,300 ($2,500–2,750)

Duart Castle

Scottish Collection (Limited Edition)

Standing proudly on the Isle of Mull, Duart Castle is the 13th-century home of the Maclean's of Duart.

Introduced in February 1992 and limited to 3,000 pieces, Duart Castle is still currently available.

Produced: 1992–
Height: 5-1/8 in./13 cm
Versions: 1
Backstamp: M
Current value: £RRP ($RRP)

Eamont Lodge

Christmas Lodge Collection

Eamont Lodge can be found at the entrance to Lowther Castle in Penrith, Cumbria. Built in 1877 of pink sandstone quarried on the estate, and roofed with Cumbrian slate, Eamont Lodge is a fine example of Victorian Gothic.

Introduced in March 1993, Eamont Lodge was the second in a series of four lodge houses. As the model was only available until the end of the year, it was retired in December 1993.

Produced: 1993
Height: 4¼ in./11 cm
Versions: 1
Backstamp: N
Current value: £50–60 ($150–200)

East Neuk

Scottish Collection

Situated in an area known as the East Neuk of Fife, which is immediately opposite Edinburgh, across the Firth of Forth, this little cottage is built of stone with a pantile roof. 'Neuk' is taken from the Old Scots and means 'a comfortable or cosy place'.

Introduced in July 1987, the model was retired in December 1991.

Produced: 1987–91
Height: 2 in./5 cm
Versions: 1
Backstamp: G
Current value: £25–30 ($40–50)

E

Edzell Summer-House

Scottish Collection

Set in the grounds of Edzell Castle, about 5 miles north of Brechin, Edzell Summer-House is a tiny pavilion which was built in 1604. Constructed of red sandstone with slate tiles (95% of which are original), the building is a marvel of Scottish architecture.

Introduced in July 1993, the model is still current.

Produced: 1993–
Height: 4 in./10 cm
Versions: 1
Backstamp: N
Current value: £RRP ($RRP)

Elm Cottage

English Collection – Midlands

Located in a village near Chippenham, Wiltshire, this small lodge house was built more than 200 years ago. Constructed of Cotswold stone, the roof is also of stone and probably weighs in excess of 2 tons; the ornately carved wooden gables are a prominent feature.

Introduced in July 1994, the model is still current.

Produced: 1994–
Height: 2¾ in./7 cm
Versions: 1
Backstamp: O
Current value: £RRP ($RRP)

Eilean Donnan Castle

Scottish Collection

Built by Alexander II of Scotland in 1220 on an island at the meeting points of Lochs Duich, Alsh and Long, Eilean Donnan Castle was bombarded by the English warship *Worcester* in 1719 and was destroyed. The ruin was rebuilt in 1932 by the MacRae family at a cost of almost £250,000, and is now a clan war memorial and museum.

Introduced in February 1990, Eilean Donnan Castle is still currently available.

Produced: 1990–
Height: 5-1/8 in./13 cm
Versions: 1
Backstamp: K
Current value: £RRP ($RRP)

E

69

Emile

Miscellaneous

Emile, one of the five-model set of clowns, was introduced in 1983. Although only available for one year, Emile – as with Danny – was remodelled. Originally, Emile was alone and the base of the model was larger; this model carried backstamp A. In the remodelled version, Emile had a dog with him and the base was smaller; this model carried backstamp C.

Emile was retired in 1984. Recorded sales of the original version are less than 100 pieces, and even though more pieces were made of the restyled version, it is still rare.

Produced: 1983–84
Height: 5–6 in./12½–15 cm
Versions: 2
Backstamp: A, C
Current value: Version 1 – £800–900 ($2,500+)
  Version 2 – £550–650 ($1,500+)

Eriskay Croft

Scottish Collection

Eriskay, a small island in the Hebrides, between Barra and South Uist, takes the full force of the Atlantic weather, so the crofts (which are affectionately known as 'black houses') are sturdily built of stone with a turf roof.

Introduced in February 1992, Eriskay Croft is still current.

Produced: 1992–
Height: 2¼ in./5½ cm
Versions: 1
Backstamp: M
Current value: £RRP
  ($RRP)

Falls Mill

American Landmarks

Falls Mill, which is very finely detailed, was introduced in June 1989 and was retired in December 1992.

Produced: 1989–92
Height: 4¾ in./12 cm
Versions: 1
Backstamp: J
Current value: £120–140
   ($200–250)

Der Familienschrein

German Collection

Der Familienschrein (The Family Chapel) was introduced in September 1988, and was retired in December 1991 after a relatively short production run.

Produced: 1988–91
Height: 4 in./10 cm
Versions: 1
Backstamp: H
Current value: £50–60 ($80–100)

Farriers

English Collection – Midlands

Based upon a cottage found in Worcestershire, in this model the farrier (who shod horses and whose trade had evolved from the blacksmith) has only a small part of his house remaining as a stable and workshop.

Introduced in July 1985, Farriers was retired in December 1990.

Produced: 1985–90
Height: 2½ in./6½ cm
Versions: 1
Backstamp: E
Current value: £40–45 ($75–100)

Farthing Lodge

English Collection – Midlands

Originally a toll-keeper's house, the windows of Farthing Lodge were positioned to give a clear view of the turnpike and approaching travellers.

Introduced in February 1991, Farthing Lodge is still current.

Produced: 1991–
Height: 2½ in./6½ cm
Versions: 1
Backstamp: L
Current value: £RRP ($RRP)

Finchingfields

English Collection – South-East

The village of Finchingfield, near Saffron Walden in Essex, is well known for its attractive blend of architecture.

Finchingfields is timber framed and thatched with Norfolk reed, but its most striking feature is the front elevation which is plastered and decorated with elaborate ornamental designs. The technique used for this form of decoration is known as pargeting.

Introduced in July 1992, the model is still currently available.

Produced: 1992–
Height: 3-3/8 in./8½ cm
Versions: 1
Backstamp: M
Current value: £RRP ($RRP)

F

Fire House 1

American Landmarks

Situated in the New England state of Maine, the Victorian architectural influence upon Fire House 1 is evident in the design of the hose-drying tower and the bell tower.

Introduced in June 1991, the model is still current.

Produced: 1991–
Height: 4¼ in./11 cm
Versions: 1
Backstamp: L
Current value: £RRP ($RRP)

Fisherman's Bothy

Scottish Collection

In a country where fishing provides a livelihood for many of the people, Fisherman's Bothy provides a summer home for the salmon fisher as he fishes in the deep sea loch.

Introduced in February 1990, this model is still current.

Produced: 1990–
Height: 2 in./5 cm
Versions: 1
Backstamp: K
Current value: £RRP ($RRP)

Fisherman's Cottage

English Collection – South-West

Reminiscent of the cottages to be found in the coves and harbours of Cornwall, these sturdy, heavily slated dwellings have withstood centuries of Atlantic storms.

Introduced in February 1985, Fisherman's Cottage was retired in December 1989.

Produced: 1985–89
Height: 2 in./5 cm
Versions: 1
Backstamp: G
Current value: £40–45 ($70–80)

Fiveways

English Collection – Midlands

Built 300 years ago, when the major routes were simple dirt tracks, cottages such as this were situated at the junctions of the tracks. Typical of the cottages to be found in Shropshire and Cheshire, Fiveways was probably the home of a craftsman who was dependent upon the passing trade.

Introduced in February 1989, the model is still current.

Produced: 1989–
Height: 2¾ in./6½ cm
Versions: 1
Backstamp: J
Current value: £RRP ($RRP)

Flower Sellers

English Collection – South-East

This timber-framed house provides a most unusual sight in London's Soho Square.

Introduced in July 1991, Flower Sellers is still current.

Produced: 1991–
Height: 4-1/8 in./10½ cm
Versions: 1
Backstamp: L
Current value: £RRP ($RRP)

Forge Barn
American Collection – 1st Series

Introduced in October 1984, only 275 pieces were produced before Forge Barn was retired in October 1985.

Produced: 1984–85
Height: 2½ in./5¾ cm
Versions: 1
Backstamp: D
Current value: £350–400 ($550–650)

Forget-me-not
Collectors Club

Forget-me-not was only available to members of the Collectors Club during the Club Year of March 1992 to February 1993.

The cottage portrayed the story of a couple who are soon to be married, and

who have just bought their first home. Although the thatched cottage is in a somewhat dilapidated condition, their intention is to renovate it and try to restore it to its former glory; there is a broken down car buried amongst the foliage; and there is a solitary badger in the undergrowth at the front of the cottage on the left. (*See also* Heaven Lea Cottage.)

Produced: 1992–93
Height: 3¼ in./9½ cm
Versions: 1
Backstamp: M
Current value: £80–100 ($150–200)

Fountains Abbey

Studley Royal Collection
(Limited Edition)

Now a part of the gardens at Studley Royal in Yorkshire, Fountains Abbey was founded by a group of Benedictine monks who came from York in 1132–33; the monks adopted Cistercian rules and founded one of the most beautiful of England's abbeys. The main Abbey buildings date from between 1150 and 1250, and the North tower was added in the early 16th century. The Abbey was incorporated into the Studley Royal gardens in 1768.

The medieval ruin is very well preserved and can be approached either by road or by a footpath through the impressive grounds of Studley Park.

Unfortunately, at the time of going to print there was very little information available concerning this model, and neither was it possible to obtain an illustration. To be introduced in January 1995, the model is expected to be limited to 5,000 pieces, and only available in the USA during that year, possibly being generally released in 1996.

Four Seasons

English Collection – Midlands

Built in the 16th century, this timber-framed house from Warwickshire has Cotswold stone at ground level to protect the timber framing from rising damp.

Introduced in February 1987, Four Seasons was retired in December 1991.

Produced: 1987–91
Height: 4 in./10 cm
Versions: 1
Backstamp: G
Current value: £55–65 ($125–150)

Foxglove Fields

English Collection — Midlands

This cottage of 17th century origin can be found near Credenhill in Herefordshire. Foxglove Fields combines stone, timber and thatch, and epitomises the local vernacular style.

Introduced in February 1993, Foxglove Fields is still currently available.

Produced: 1993–
Height: 3¼ in./8 cm
Versions: 1
Backstamp: N
Current value: £RRP ($RRP)

The Gables

English Collection – South-East

Typical of the Gothic style of architecture which flourished in the 19th century through the efforts of Prince Albert, Consort of Queen Victoria, this Victorian family house is aptly named with its carved gables and front porch.

Introduced in February 1987, The Gables was retired in December 1992.

Produced: 1987–92
Height: 5¼ in./13½ cm
Versions: 1
Backstamp: G
Current value: £100–120 ($200–250)

Gamekeeper's Cottage

Miscellaneous

Gamekeeper's Cottage can be found on the estate of Ragley Hall in Warwickshire, and was built in 1872 by the 5th Marquess of Hertford.

When 350 pieces were first released at the South Bend Show in the USA, Gamekeeper's Cottage had a red roof and a special stamp SOUTH BEND 1991. The cottage was then issued in July 1991 as a Collectors Club events cottage; it had a different coloured roof, and the front door and flowers were painted in the colours of the members choice. The cottage was retired in September 1992.

Produced: 1991–92
Height: 3½ in./9 cm
Versions: 2 (excluding personalisation)
Backstamp: L
Current value:
  Version 1 – £175–225 ($200–250)
  Version 2 – £50–60 ($85–115)

Gardener's Cottage

Collectors Club

Introduced in March 1991 as an exclusive cottage only available for one year to members of the Collectors Club, it was retired in February 1992.

Produced: 1991–92
Height: 3¾ in./9½ cm
Versions: 1
Backstamp: L
Current value: £100–120
  ($150–200)

Das Gebirgskirchlein

German Collection

With its onion-shaped towers, wooden tiles and plain white walls, Das Gebirgskirchlein is typical of the buildings seen on the borders of southern Germany and Austria.

Introduced in February 1987, the model is still current.

Produced: 1987–
Height: 5-1/8 in./13 cm
Versions: 1
Backstamp: G
Current value: £RRP ($RRP)

G

General Store

American Collection – 1st Series

Introduced in October 1984, the initial production pieces of General Store had a diagonal, ribbed store sign with lettering in red. At some time during production (which was only for a year), the store sign changed to a horizontal, timber-mounted sign with white embossed lettering, larger and easier to read than the initial red lettering.

General Store was retired in October 1985; only 150 pieces were produced, the original version being the rarest.

Produced: 1984–85
Height: 2¾ in./7 cm
Versions: 2
Backstamp: D
Current value:
  Version 1 – £375–450 ($600–750)
  Version 2 – £325–375 ($525–575)

Gingerbread Shop

Christmas Collection

The Christmas Collection adopts the theme of a traditional village at Christmastime, and the Gingerbread Shop portrays the baker's shop, a popular place at Christmastime, where the villagers stock up in readiness for the festivities.

Introduced in February 1993, Gingerbread Shop was another of the models to feature the new 'icing sugar' snow; the model is still current.

Produced: 1993–
Height: 2½ in./6½ cm
Versions: 1
Backstamp: N
Current value: £RRP ($RRP)

Glenlochie Lodge

Scottish Collection

The highland lodge, reflecting a grand baronial style, stands at the entrance to the laird's estate, where each year the local highland games are held.

Introduced in February 1990, Glenlochie Lodge was retired in December 1993.

Produced: 1990–93
Height: 4¾ in./12 cm
Versions: 2
Backstamp: K
Current value: £45–55
   ($120–150)

Gold Miner's Claim

American Landmarks

Bringing back memories of the days when thousands of prospectors hoped to 'strike it lucky' panning for gold, Gold Miner's Claim shows the disused mine, derelict cabin and rusting equipment which were left behind once the mine ran out.

Introduced in June 1992, the model is still current. However, approximately 15 pieces were released from the factory without the 'snow'. Although retailers were asked to return the pieces for the 'snow' to be added, it is not known if they were all returned, or whether some were actually sold; if so, these pieces could be valuable.

Produced: 1992–
Height: 3¼ in./8 cm
Versions: 1
Backstamp: M
Current value: £RRP ($RRP)

G

Granny Smiths

English Collection – Midlands

Surrounded by Worcestershire orchards, this 16th-century cottage typifies the architecture of the area. Launched in February 1992, Granny Smiths is current.

Produced: 1992–
Height: 2¾ in./7 cm
Versions: 1
Backstamp: M
Current value: £RRP ($RRP)

Grantchester Meadows

*English Collection –
South-East*

Grantchester Meadows is
an 18th-century timber-
framed cottage, situated
in a little hamlet close to
Cambridge. The hamlet
has long been a favourite
haunt of both students
and dons. Reached by a
bridge over a tributary of
the River Cam, the cottage is roofed
with East Anglian thatch and is surrounded by meadows.

Introduced in July 1992 and still current, the model is finely detailed, including willows, a swan and a punt.

Produced: 1992–
Height: 4 in./10 cm
Versions: 1
Backstamp: M
Current value: £RRP ($RRP)

Great Point Light

American Landmarks

Built in 1818, this lighthouse stood firm
until in 1984 it was brought down by a
very severe storm.

Introduced in March 1990, Great
Point Light (which is only the second
lighthouse to have been produced by
Lilliput Lane), is still current.

Produced: 1990–
Height: 4 in./10 cm
Versions: 1
Backstamp: K
Current value: £RRP ($RRP)

The Greengrocer's
Village Shops Collection

Based upon traditional Cotswold stores, The Greengrocer's was one of the first three models launched in a series of six. Introduced in October 1991, the model is still current. (In the UK, the model was initially exclusive to the UK Guild of Specialist China & Glass Retailers before general release.)

Produced: 1991–
Height: 3¾ in./9½ cm
Versions: 1
Backstamp: L
Current value: £RRP ($RRP)

G

Greensted Church
English Collection – South-East

St Andrew's, at Greensted-juxta-Ongar in Essex, certainly dates from 845 AD, and could even date from 645 AD. An outstanding example of a Saxon church, it is unique in having its original split oak log walls intact, and is believed to be the

oldest wooden church in the world as well as the oldest surviving example of timber framing in England.

Introduced in February 1989, Greensted Church is still current.

Produced: 1989–
Height: 4 in./10¼ cm
Versions: 1
Backstamp: J
Current value: £RRP ($RRP)

Grist Mill

American Collection – 1st Series

Although introduced in October 1984, due to the lack of popularity of the American Collection, all thirteen of the models in the Collection were retired in October 1985. As a result very few pieces were produced and hence each model is quite rare. When it was retired in October 1985, only 150 pieces had been made of Grist Mill.

Produced: 1984–85
Height: 2½ in./6½ cm
Versions: 1
Backstamp: D
Current value: £375–475 ($600–750)

Grist Mill: front view (left); side view (right)

Guildhall

Miscellaneous

Commissioned in the UK by the UK Guild of Specialist China & Glass Retailers for sale exclusively in their stores, Guildhall was introduced in July 1987 and retired in December 1989.

Produced: 1987–89
Height: 5 in./12½ cm
Versions: 1
Backstamp: G
Current value: £100–150
    ($200–250)

Gulliver 1986

Miscellaneous

Gulliver's Travels was written by Jonathan Swift in 1726 as a satire on contemporary politics. Lemuel Gulliver, the hero of the tale, was shipwrecked on the island of Lilliput, the inhabitants of which were 6 inches high.

Introduced in February 1986, the model shows Gulliver tied to the ground by the Lilliputians. Initial production pieces had the backstamp positioned on the front, although at some point the backstamp was repositioned on the rear (it is thought that collectors were unhappy with the positioning of the backstamp on the front). The model was retired in December 1986.

Produced: 1986
Height: 3 in./7½ cm
Versions: 2
Backstamp: F
Current value:
  Version 1 – £250–325 ($350–400)
  Version 2 – £200–250 ($225–275)

Gulliver's Gate
Miscellaneous

Gulliver's Gate is based upon crenellated stone walls at Kirkoswald near Penrith, Cumbria. Introduced in February 1994 and still current, Gulliver's Gate could be regarded as a point-of-sale item, but it has proved popular with collectors (as did Scroll on the Wall).

Produced: 1994–
Height: 3¼ in./8 cm
Versions: 1
Backstamp: O
Current value: £RRP ($RRP)

Harvest Mill

American Landmarks
(Limited Edition)

Based upon the Old Mill at Pigeon Forge in Tennessee, which has been a working mill for over 160 years, Harvest Mill was introduced in January 1994. Limited to 3,500 pieces, the model was only available in North America during 1994; however, it is expected to be generally available from 1995.

Produced: 1994—
Height: 4¼ in./11 cm
Versions: 1
Backstamp: O
Current value: £Not known
    ($RRP)

Haus im Rheinland

German Collection

Haus im Rheinland is typical of the buildings to be found in the land of the Lorelei – a large rock in the River Rhine near Sankt Goarshausen – where according to legend a beautiful maiden was said to have drowned herself in despair, only to rise as a siren to lure fishermen to their doom on the rock.

Introduced in February 1987, this model is still current.

Produced: 1987–
Height: 7 in./18 cm
Versions: 1
Backstamp: G
Current value: £RRP ($RRP)

Heaven Lea Cottage

Collectors Club

Heaven Lea Cottage continues the story which began with Forget-me-not. The newlyweds have now renovated the cottage to its former glory and renamed it Heaven Lea Cottage; the car has been restored and now sits proudly outside the cottage; and the family of badgers are more than pleased with their new surroundings.

Introduced in March 1993, Heaven Lea Cottage was exclusive to Collectors Club members, and was retired in February 1994.

Produced: 1993–94
Height: 3¼ in./9½ cm
Versions: 1
Backstamp: N
Current value: £60–80 ($160–200)

Hebridean Hame

Scottish Collection

Originally a 'black house' which had no windows or chimney (smoke from the peat fire just filtered through the thatch, which was replaced each year), this sturdy cottage from the Outer Hebrides, has had windows and chimneys added later. Introduced in February 1990, it was retired in December 1992.

Produced: 1990–92
Height: 2-3/8 in./6 cm
Versions: 1
Backstamp: K
Current value: £35–40 ($70–90)

Hegarty's Home
Irish Collection

Typical of the buildings in County Donegal, this working family home might also have served as a hideaway for the drinking of poteen (the illicit alcohol made from potatoes).

Introduced in July 1989, the model was retired in December 1992.

Produced: 1989–92
Height: 2-1/8 in./
  5½ cm
Versions: 1
Backstamp: J
Current value: £40–50
  ($80–100)

Helmere Cottage
English Collection – Northern

With its distinctive green slate roof, Helmere Cottage can be found in the Lakeland fells.

Introduced in July 1989, Helmere Cottage is still currently available.

Produced: 1989–
Height: 3¼ in./8 cm
Versions: 1
Backstamp: J
Current value: £RRP
  ($RRP)

Hermitage
Welsh Collection

From around 150 BC Anglesey has been the centre of Celtic culture and religion, and the island is still remembered as the place where the Druids made the fiercest stand against their Roman conquerors. Hermitage can be found in a remote corner of the island, and although in poor repair has provided shelter for its various occupants over the past 200 years.

Introduced in July 1985, Hermitage was remodelled in December 1986. Major changes were made including an extension being added to the main building, more foliage around the base, repositioning of the steps leading up to the cottage; the second version was also larger in size than the original version.

Hermitage was retired in December 1990.

Produced: 1985–90
Height: 2½ in./6½ cm; version 1 smaller
Versions: 2
Backstamp: E, G
Current value:
   Version 1 – £150–200 ($250–300)
   Version 2 – £60–80 ($50–75)

Front view: version 1 (left); version 2 (right)

Back view: version 1 (left); version 2 (right)

High Ghyll Farm

English Collection – Northern

Using an amalgam of various farm buildings which can still be found in the Lake District today, High Ghyll Farm shows how a typical Cumbrian farm would have appeared in the last century.

Introduced in July 1992, High Ghyll Farm is still currently available.

Produced: 1992–
Height: 5 in./12½ cm
Versions: 1
Backstamp: M
Current value: £RRP ($RRP)

Highland Lodge

Christmas Lodge Collection

Built around the 1850s, Highland Lodge can be found close to the Highland village of Kinloch Laggan. Constructed of local stone and roofed with slate, the most striking feature of the lodge is the round tower which is topped with a conical roof.

Introduced in February 1992, Highland Lodge was the first model in the Christmas Lodge Collection. Only available during that year, the model was retired in December 1992.

Produced: 1992
Height: 5¼ in./13½ cm
Versions: 1
Backstamp: M
Current value: £90–120
($220–250)

Holly Cottage

English Collection – Northern

Holly Cottage is based upon a small Victorian cottage to be found in that part of Cumbria which was formerly Westmorland (which was combined with Cumberland to form Cumbria).

Introduced in February 1983, Holly Cottage was remodelled in July 1984, when the height of the chimneys was reduced, the base around the conservatory was made thinner, and a door frame was added around the door.

Other noticeable differences between the two versions were that the original version was duller in colour and was also less refined in appearance than the remodelled version.

Front view: version 1 (left); version 2 (right). In particular, notice the height of the chimneys, and the thickness of the base around the conservatory

Holly Cottage was retired in December 1988.

Produced: 1983–88
Height: 3 in./7½ cm
Versions: 2

Backstamp: B, D
Current value:
   Version 1 – £350–450
    ($1,200–1,500)
   Version 2 – £60–80 ($85–125)

H

Hollytree House

Christmas Collection

Introduced in February 1992 as part of the miniature Christmas Collection, Hollytree House continued the theme of a traditional village at Christmastime. Hollytree House is still currently available.

Produced: 1992–
Height: 2-3/8 in./6 cm
Versions: 1
Backstamp: N
Current value: £RRP ($RRP)

Holme Dyke

English Collection – Northern

This house is typical of those built in the 17th century in the vicinity of York. The walls are of local stone and it is tiled with Flemish pantiles.

Introduced in February 1987, Holme Dyke was retired in December 1990.

Produced: 1987–90
Height: 2½ in./6½ cm
Versions: 1
Backstamp: G
Current value: £40–50 ($70–90)

Home Sweet Home

American Landmarks

The early American settlers made good use of the abundant supply of natural materials available to them – especially the vast tracts of timber – and so a log cabin came to represent a typical home in those early days of colonisation.

Introduced in January 1992, Home Sweet Home is still currently available.

Produced: 1992–
Height: 3-3/8 in./8½ cm
Versions: 1
Backstamp: M
Current value: £RRP ($RRP)

Christmas Specials

Deer Park Hall, 1988–89 (left), and Yuletide Inn, 1990–91 (right)

Drapers

From the English Collection – Midlands;
one of the rarest models, produced 1982–83

The Gables

From the English Collection –
South-East, produced 1987–92

Guildhall

Commissioned by the
UK Guild of Specialist
China & Glass Retailers,
produced 1987–89

Hometown Depot
American Landmarks

Situated alongside the railroad somewhere in Indiana, this station revives memories of the days when the train was the only means that people had of travelling long distances.

Introduced in March 1990, Hometown Depot was retired in December 1993.

Produced: 1990–93
Height: 3 in./7½ cm
Versions: 1
Backstamp: K
Current value: £60–70
($100–125)

Honeysuckle Cottage
English Collection – South-East

Based upon a 17th-century thatched cottage in the village of Oakhanger in Hampshire, this building is quite a substantial house for its time. The oak frame would have been in-filled with clay on oak staves and then painted with lime wash. When the roof comes down to ground level and almost touches the floor, it is known as a 'catslide' roof.

Honeysuckle Cottage was among the very first Lilliput Lane models to be introduced in September

Front view of version 2 of Honeysuckle Cottage

The version 1 cottages on the left and right show the variations in colouring that occurred, and the version 2 cottage (centre) shows the change in the thickness of the base

1982, and soon proved to be a very popular model. Prior to December 1983 slight modifications were made to the colour of the building and to the dog, and it is thought that there could have been up to five variations produced. However, in December 1983 the cottage was remodelled, with the base appearing thinner and more refined.

Honeysuckle Cottage was retired in December 1987.

Produced: 1982–87
Height: 2¾ in./7 cm
Versions: 2
Backstamp: B, C, D
Current value:
Version 1 – £350–450 ($1,200–1,500)
Version 2 – £70–90 ($125–175)

Honeysuckle Cottage 1992
Anniversary

Based upon the original Honeysuckle Cottage, this model was produced to commemorate the 10th anniversary of the launch of Lilliput Lane.

Introduced in February 1992, it was only available until December of that year.

Produced: 1992
Height: 2¾ in./7 cm
Versions: 1
Backstamp: M
Current value: £130–160 ($195–225)

Hopcroft Cottage

English Collection – South-East

The neat mid-Victorian village of Old Warden in Bedfordshire was rebuilt by the last Lord Ongley (who died in 1877) as a model village for his tenants.

Hopcroft Cottage, based upon a building in Old Warden, was introduced in July 1991, and is still currently available.

Produced: 1991–
Height: 4 in./10 cm
Versions: 1
Backstamp: L
Current value: £RRP ($RRP)

H

Inglewood

English Collection – Northern

Buildings similar to Inglewood can be found in the fertile farming land to the west and north of York. The cottage has hardly changed since it was originally built of York stone with a pantiled roof.

Introduced in July 1987, Inglewood was remodelled in December 1989 when a window at the rear was removed, and the model was made slightly larger; the windows on the remodelled version were also more pronounced and more finely detailed. Inglewood was retired in July 1994.

Produced: 1987–94
Height: 2 in./5 cm
Versions: 2
Backstamp: G, J
Current value:
  Version 1 – £20–30 ($45–65)
  Version 2 – £15–20 ($30–40)

Front view: version 2 (left); version 1 (right)

Back view: version 2 (left); version 1 (right)

Inverlochie Hame

Scottish Collection

To be found on the west coast of the Scottish Highlands and Islands region, this fisherman's cottage is a rugged building solidly constructed of granite to provide protection from the Atlantic weather.

Introduced in February 1989, Inverlochie Hame is still currently available.

Produced: 1989–
Height: 2½ in./6 cm
Versions: 1
Backstamp: J
Current value: £RRP ($RRP)

Ivy House

Annual Ornament

Ivy House was the third in the Annual Ornament collection. Introduced in February 1994, the model was only available until December of that year.

Produced: 1994
Height: 3 in./7½ cm
Versions: 1
Backstamp: O
Current value: £RRP ($RRP)

I

Izaak Walton's Cottage
English Collection – Midlands

Izaak Walton (1593–1683) is well-known as the 'father' of fly fishing and the author of *The Compleat Angler*. Born in Stafford (at 92 Eastgate Street), Walton later lived in a half-timbered cottage at Shallowford, with the River Meece flowing through the grounds. He gave his cottage to the town of Stafford and it is kept as a memorial to him.

Lilliput Lane have portrayed the cottage as they believe it would have looked in Izaak Walton's days, with the origi-nal thatch. The model was introduced in July 1987, and for the first twelve months was exclusive to Church's China in the UK, before becoming generally available. Izaak Walton's Cottage was retired in December 1989.

Produced: 1987–89
Height: 3½ in./9 cm
Versions: 1
Backstamp: G
Current value: £70–85 ($95–115)

Jagdhütte

German Collection

A building where hunters gather to eat, drink and practice blowing their horns in readiness for the festival parades, Jagdhütte was introduced in February 1987 and is still currently available.

Produced: 1987–
Height: 4½ in./11½ cm
Versions: 1
Backstamp: G
Current value: £RRP ($RRP)

Jasmine Cottage

Classics Collection

The entire range of miniature cottages in the Classics Collection is based upon the buildings to be found in Blaise Hamlet, at Henbury, near Bristol.

Jasmine Cottage is one of three thatched cottages in the hamlet, and John Nash's early designs refer to it as 'Dutch Cottage', but no-one knows why its name was changed.

Introduced in February 1993, Jasmine Cottage is due to be retired in March 1995.

Produced: 1993–95
Height: 2¾ in./6 cm
Versions: 1
Backstamp: N
Current value: £RRP ($RRP)

Jasmine Cottage

English Collection — South-West

Based upon the buildings at Blaise Hamlet near Bristol, Jasmine Cottage — one of the three thatched cottages in the hamlet — is situated between Diamond Cottage and Double Cottage, and its unusual double thatched roof provides an interesting contrast to the slate roofs of its neighbours.

Introduced in February 1991, Jasmine Cottage is still current.

Produced: 1991–
Height: 5 in./12½ cm
Versions: 1
Backstamp: L
Current value: £RRP ($RRP)

John Barleycorn Cottage

English Collection — South-East

John Barleycorn Cottage is another of the cottages based upon buildings in the mid-Victorian village of Old Warden, near Biggleswade, in Bedfordshire. Old Warden was rebuilt in its present form by the last Lord Ongley as a model village for his tenants.

Introduced in July 1991, John Barleycorn Cottage is due to be retired in March 1995.

Produced: 1991–95
Height: 4¼ in./11 cm
Versions: 1
Backstamp: L
Current value: £RRP ($RRP)

John Knox House

Scottish Collection

Situated within Edinburgh's Royal Mile (the name given to the ancient streets which run eastwards from Castle Street to the gates of Holyroodhouse), John Knox House is a 15th-century building where Knox, the leader of the Protestant Reformation in Scotland, is believed to have lived. The house has a timber gallery and is now preserved as a museum.

Introduced in July 1989, the model was retired in December 1992.

Produced: 1989–92
Height: 5¾ in./14½ cm
Versions: 1
Backstamp: J
Current value: £45–55 ($80–100)

Jones the Butcher

Village Shops Collection

A sub-collection to the English Collection – Midlands, the Village Shops Collection is based upon traditional Cotswold stores. Introduced in July 1993, the model is still current. (In the UK, it was initially exclusive to the UK Guild of Specialist China & Glass Retailers before general release.)

Produced: 1993–
Height: 3¾ in./9½ cm
Versions: 1
Backstamp: N
Current value: £RRP ($RRP)

J

Junk and Disorderly

English Collection — Midlands

Pembridge is a village in Herefordshire which still has a wide and varied selection of ancient buildings. One of these buildings is a medieval cross-passage Hall which was built in 1382. Known as 'Junk and Disorderly', part of the building is used to sell local crafts and items of bric-a-brac.

Introduced in February 1993, this model is still current.

Produced: 1993–
Height: 4 in./10 cm
Versions: 1
Backstamp: N
Current value: £RRP ($RRP)

Keeper's Lodge

English Collection – Northern

Similar to the many gatekeepers' houses which can be found at the entrances to large country estates, this small Victorian cottage displays many of the features of the Gothic style which was so popular in the 19th century. Built of stone, an interesting feature is the small tower.

Introduced in February 1987, the model was retired in December 1988.

Produced: 1987–88
Height: 3½ in./9 cm
Versions: 1
Backstamp: G
Current value: £60–80 ($125–150)

Kenmore Cottage

Scottish Collection

Kenmore, a picturesque village at the eastern end of Loch Tay, was built by the philanthropist the Marquis of Breadalbane. Kenmore Cottage, which is based upon the Victorian Rustic style, was introduced in July 1989 and was retired in July 1993.

Produced: 1989–93
Height: 3-3/8 in./8½ cm
Versions: 1
Backstamp: J
Current value: £40–60
($100–125)

Kennedy Homestead
Irish Collection

In 1820, Patrick Kennedy was born in a small stone cottage in Dunganstown, County Wexford. When he emigrated to America in 1849, little did he realise that he was to become the founding father of the Kennedy 'dynasty', and that his great-grandson – John F Kennedy – would become one of America's best-remembered Presidents.

Kennedy Homestead, introduced in July 1989 and still current, is based upon the small stone cottage that Patrick Kennedy left in 1849 and which is now a major tourist attraction.

Produced: 1989–
Height: 2¼ in./5½ cm
Versions: 1
Backstamp: J
Current value: £RRP ($RRP)

Kentish Oast House
English Collection – South-East

Based upon a derelict building near Tunbridge Wells in Kent, oast houses with circular kilns were introduced in the early 1800s, but around 1900 square kilns became more normal.

Introduced in July 1985, and using 7,500 tiles to cover the roof and the drying kilns, the original version had a metal cowl on the roof; however, from December 1986 the cowl was made of plastic. Kentish Oast House was retired in December 1990.

Produced: 1985–90
Height: 3¾ in./9½ cm
Versions: 2
Backstamp: E
Current value:
    Version 1 – £65–75 ($120–135)
    Version 2 – £50–60 ($85–115)

Kilmore Quay

Irish Collection

Kilmore Quay is typical of the attractive little cottages that the fishermen of County Wexford live in.

Introduced in July 1989, Kilmore Quay was retired in December 1992.

Produced: 1989–92
Height: 2¾ in./7 cm
Versions: 1
Backstamp: J
Current value: £45–55 ($80–100)

The King's Arms

English Collection – South-East

Based upon the coaching inns which once stood beside the Great North Road (from London to York), when The King's Arms was introduced in June 1990 demand for the model was so great that it was not readily available until January 1991; the model is still current.

Produced: 1990–
Height: 5½ in./14 cm
Versions: 1
Backstamp: K
Current value: £RRP ($RRP)

Kinlochness
Scottish Collection

A typical gamekeeper's lodge built of granite with a slate roof and crow-stepped gables, Kinlochness was introduced in February 1990 and was retired in July 1993.

Produced: 1990–93
Height: 4 in./10 cm
Versions: 1
Backstamp: K
Current value: £35–45 ($80–100)

Kirkbrae Cottage
Scottish Collection

Situated in Banffshire, Kirkbrae Cottage is a hillside cottage with attractive views of the rocky coastline.

Introduced in February 1990, the model was retired in July 1993.

Produced: 1990–93
Height: 2-3/8 in./6 cm
Versions: None
Backstamp: K
Current value: £35–45 ($70–90)

Die Kleine Backerei
German Collection

This typical 17th-century German bakehouse would serve a dozen farms and was located away from the main house to avoid the danger of fire.

Introduced in September 1988, the model was retired in July 1994.

Produced: 1988–94
Height: 3-3/8 in./8½ cm
Versions: 1
Backstamp: H
Current value: £25–30 ($60–80)

K

Lace Lane

English Collection –
Midlands

Nottingham is renowned as the 'City of Lace', and this classic 15th century timber-framed building is now a museum to the city's lace industry.

Introduced in July 1991, Lace Lane is still currently available.

Produced: 1991–
Height: 4 in./10 cm
Versions: 1
Backstamp: L
Current value: £RRP ($RRP)

Ladybank Lodge

Scottish Collection

Based upon a building which can be found in the village of Ladybank, north of Glenrothes, in Fife, Ladybank Lodge was built during the mid-19th century. Built of ironstone with a slate roof, it has the usual Scottish feature of crow-stepped gables, one of which leads into the round tower.

Introduced in July 1994, the model is still currently available.

Produced: 1994–
Height: 3½ in./9 cm
Versions: 1
Backstamp: O
Current value: £RRP ($RRP)

Lakeside House

English Collection – Northern

Version 2, with some of the windows removed

As the Lake District became increasingly popular amongst the Victorians as an area to visit, so many new dwellings were built – using local stone and slate – to provide accommodation for them. The houses were substantially built and many are still in use today as guest houses.

Introduced in September 1982, Lakeside House was restyled in February 1983, when some of the windows were removed (to save on the time required to paint the model) and the model itself was simplified. Examples of the original version (which carried backstamp A) are quite rare and hence are difficult to find.

Lakeside House was retired in April 1986.

Produced: 1982–86
Height: 3½ in./9 cm
Versions: 2
Backstamp: A, B
Current value: Version 1 – £900–1,200 ($2,000–2,500)
  Version 2 – £400–500 ($1,000–1,250)

L

Lapworth Lock

English Collection – Midlands

On the Lapworth section of the Stratford-upon-Avon Canal, there are six of these delightful barrel-roofed cottages to be seen. The roofs were constructed in the same way as the bridges and tunnels on the canal. Introduced in February 1991, Lapworth Lock was retired in December 1993.

Produced: 1991–93
Height: 2¾ in./6½ cm
Versions: 1
Backstamp: L
Current value: £35–45 ($90–125)

Lavender Cottage

Collectors Club

Based upon cottages to be found in Bishops Cannings, Wiltshire, Lavender Cottage is a small thatched cottage built of Cotswold stone in the 16th/17th century.

Introduced in October 1989, Lavender Cottage was offered exclusively to members of the Lilliput Lane Collectors Club; it was retired in February 1991.

Produced: 1989–91
Height: 2¾ in./7 cm
Versions: 1
Backstamp: J
Current value: £75–95 ($100–150)

Leagrave Cottage

Special Events

Leagrave Cottage was based upon a building to be seen at the Chiltern Open Air Museum in Buckinghamshire, where a number of traditional buildings from the Buckinghamshire area, which are no longer needed, have been re-erected.

Launched at the Lilliput Lane Annual Fair, which was held in September 1994 at the Chiltern Open Air Museum, Leagrave Cottage was only available at that meeting and at the other special events held during the twelve months from September 1994; it will be retired in September 1995.

Produced: 1994–95
Height: 3-3/8 in./8½ cm
Versions: 1
Backstamp: O
Current value: £RRP ($RRP)

Leonora's Secret

Limited Edition

Leonora's Secret depicts a magnificent walled garden where a young woman finds peace and seclusion as she contemplates her future. The dilemma she has is whether she should marry for love or please her father and marry his choice of suitor.

Introduced in July 1994, Leonora's Secret was a very finely detailed model which was time-consuming and complex to produce. Because of this it was limited to 2,500 pieces world-wide, which were allocated on a 'first come, first served' basis. It is believed that the edition was fully subscribed by the end of 1994.

Produced: 1994
Height: 4½ in./11½ cm
Versions: 1
Backstamp: O
Current value: £RRP ($RRP)

Lighthouse

American Collection – 1st Series

As with the other models in the American Collection, Lighthouse was in production for a fairly short period of time. As a result, it is believed that only 200 pieces were produced from the time it was introduced (in October 1984), until it was retired (in October 1985).

Produced: 1984–85
Height: 4 in./10 cm
Versions: 1
Backstamp: D
Current value: £500–600 ($900–1,200)

Limerick House

Irish Collection

In Adare, County Limerick, the villagers represent a good cross-section of society, so it is likely that Limerick House would have been owned by a well-to-do family.

Introduced in July 1989, the model was retired in July 1992.

Produced: 1989–92
Height: 3¾ in./9½ cm
Versions: 1
Backstamp: J
Current value:
  £55–65 ($125–150)

Little Lost Dog

Collectors Club

Little Lost Dog showed a sheepdog standing beside a signpost indicating the way to London and the way to Penrith (the home of Lilliput Lane). The model was offered as a free gift to members who joined the Collectors Club during the twelve months from March 1987 to February 1988.

Although Little Lost Dog was only available during those twelve months, two versions were produced. Originally, the hole in the circle at the top of the post was quite small, and the lettering on the direction pointers was painted black. The second version had a larger hole in the centre of the circle, and the lettering appeared grey in comparison to the original.

There is some debate that another version existed which had the distances in miles given under the destinations on the signpost, and the post had an extra section between the pointers and the circle at the top. There is no firm information on this; however, it is possible that it may have been a prototype version.

Some – but not all – of the pieces distributed contained a verse inside the box:

Little Lost Dog

*Our little dog sat by the post
The words he couldn't unravel,
He unfortunately took the London Road
And far he had to travel.*

*But now he's safely found his home
I'm very glad to say,
And never more will search or roam,
Now he's with you, we're sure he'll stay.*

Just under 7,000 pieces of Little Lost Dog were produced and given to members during its production life of March 1987 to February 1988.

Produced: 1987–88
Height: 2½ in./6½ cm
Versions: 2
Backstamp: None used
Current value:
    Version 1 – £300–325 ($350–400)
    Version 2 – £220–260 ($200–300)

L

Locmaria

French Collection

Locmaria (Mary Cottage), with its strong granite walls and 'eyebrow' roof window, can be found in southwest Brittany, which is still an area of distinctive Celtic culture.

Introduced in September 1990, the model is still currently available.

Produced: 1990–
Height: 4 in./10 cm
Versions: 1
Backstamp: K
Current value: £RRP ($RRP)

Log Cabin

American Collection – 1st Series

Introduced in October 1984, Log Cabin was produced in two versions. Originally, the model had snow on it; however, the second version did not have snow.

When it was retired in October 1985, only 150 pieces of Log Cabin had been produced, of which the original version is the rarest.

Produced: 1984–85
Height: 1¾ in./4½ cm
Versions: 2
Backstamp: D
Current value:
   Version 1 – £400–475 ($700–900)
   Version 2 – £275–350 ($500–600)

Magilligan's

Irish Collection

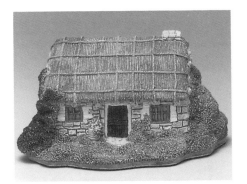

This simple two-bedroomed house in County Derry would have been a typical home for a family of labourers.

Introduced in July 1989, the model is still currently available.

Produced: 1989–
Height: 2 in./5 cm
Versions: 1
Backstamp: J
Current value: £RRP ($RRP)

Magpie Cottage

English Collection – Midlands

Typical of the Herefordshire area, this cruck-framed cottage has wattle and daub infills of the timber frame, which have then been lime-washed to provide additional weather protection. The small extension would have been added at a later date.

Introduced in February 1987, Magpie Cottage was retired in December 1990.

Produced: 1987–90
Height: 3¼ in./8 cm
Versions: 1
Backstamp: G
Current value: £55–65 ($80–100)

Mail Pouch Barn

American Landmarks

One of the first group of four models introduced in the American Landmarks collection in June 1989, Mail Pouch Barn showed a typical tobacco factory that mail carriers would often stop at for a 'chew', as well as taking a little bit extra for their 'mail pouch'.

Introduced in June 1989, Mail Pouch Barn was retired in December 1993.

Produced: 1989–93
Height: 3¼ in./8 cm
Versions: 1
Backstamp: J
Current value: £60–70 ($125–150)

Mair Haven

Scottish Collection

These sturdy fishermen's cottages are typical of the properties to be found in the villages on the eastern side of Scotland, along the North Sea coastline.

Introduced in February 1992, Mair Haven is still currently available.

Produced: 1992–
Height: 2½ in./6½ cm
Versions: 1
Backstamp: M
Current value: £RRP ($RRP)

Le Manoir de Champfleuri
French Collection

Situated in the beautiful Loire Valley, Le Manoir de Champfleuri (Pasture Lodge) marks the entrance to a Duke's estate. Built in the 18th century, the lodge has the same charm and elegance as the many chateaux which are to be found in the surrounding area.

Introduced in September 1990, the model is still current.

Produced: 1990–
Height: 6¾ in./17 cm
Versions: 1
Backstamp: K
Current value: £RRP ($RRP)

Marigold Meadow
English Collection – South-East

Based upon a cottage in Hampshire, Marigold Meadow is a 14th century oak-framed building with wattle and daub infill (although some has been replaced with brick), and a half-hip thatched roof. The large brick chimney houses a bread oven which the original occupier would have used to good effect.

Introduced in July 1993, the model is still current.

Produced: 1993–
Height: 3-3/8 in./8½ cm
Versions: 1
Backstamp: N
Current value: £RRP ($RRP)

Le Mas du Vigneron

French Collection

Le Mas du Vigneron (The Vine Grower's House) can be found on the high slopes of Provence where fine wines have been produced for centuries. Built from local stone and covered with yellow plaster, the house is reminiscent of the villas that were built here by the Romans, when the Roman civilisation spread throughout Provence in 10 BC.

Introduced in September 1990, the model is still current.

Produced: 1990–
Height: 3½ in./9 cm
Versions: 1
Backstamp: K
Current value: £RRP ($RRP)

La Maselle de Nadaillac

French Collection

La Maselle de Nadaillac (Nadaillac Shelter) can be found among the forests of the Dordogne. Built of local limestone, the thick walls support the weight of large stone slabs which make up the roof; the conical building now houses the family pig.

Introduced in September 1990, the model is still current.

Produced: 1990–
Height: 4 in./10 cm
Versions: 1
Backstamp: K
Current value: £RRP ($RRP)

Mayflower House

Miscellaneous

Produced exclusively for sale in the USA, Mayflower House was introduced in April 1989. The model had a fairly short production run before being retired in December 1990.

Mayflower House is a difficult model to obtain in the UK because of the distribution and production limitations mentioned above.

Produced: 1989–90
Height: 4¾ in./12 cm
Versions: 1
Backstamp: J
Current value: £250–350
  ($150–200)

M

Meersburger Weinstube

German Collection

Overlooking Lake Constance (also known as the Bodensee) between Germany and Switzerland, this house is bedecked with flowers.

Introduced in February 1987, the model is still currently available.

Produced: 1987–
Height: 4¾ in./12 cm
Versions: 1
Backstamp: G
Current value: £RRP ($RRP)

Micklegate Antiques

English Collection – Northern

Midwest Barn

American Collection – 1st Series

This distinctive country barn, with its red and white striped boarding, was introduced in October 1984. Seemingly one of the more popular models in the American Collection, 400 pieces had been produced by the time it was retired in October 1985.

Produced: 1984–85
Height: 2½ in./6½ cm
Versions: 1
Backstamp: D
Current value: £275–300 ($400–500)

Micklegate Antiques is typical of the 17th-century buildings to be found in the Shambles (from the Old English *shamel*, meaning a slaughterhouse), in York. A favourite place for visitors to the city, across the short, narrow Shambles old timber-framed buildings lean towards one another.

Introduced in February 1991, Micklegate Antiques is still currently available.

Produced: 1991–
Height: 4¼ in./11 cm
Versions: 1
Backstamp: L
Current value: £RRP ($RRP)

Millers

English Collection – South-East

Miners

English Collection – Northern

This two-roomed cottage, with its shiplap weatherboard and brick quoins, is typical of the buildings to be found in Kent. As only soft stone was available for building, subsequently a large amount of wood was used for the external skin.

Introduced in February 1983, Millers was remodelled during the same year, when it was made smaller and the base became more pitted. The original version carried backstamp A, whereas version 2 carried backstamp C. Millers was retired in December 1986.

Produced: 1983–86
Height: 2½ in./6½ cm; version 1 larger
Versions: 2
Backstamp: A, C
Current value:
   Version 1 – £175–225 ($250–350)
   Version 2 – £120–140 ($125–175)

Introduced in February 1983, Miners was originally all-grey in colour. In July 1983, the building was repainted in beige with an olive/sandy coloured roof; however, at the same time, a third version painted beige with a black roof was introduced. Both of these colourways were produced until the model was retired in July 1985.

Produced: 1983–85
Height: 2¾ in./7 cm
Versions: 3
Backstamp: A, C
Current value:
   Version 1 – £300–400 ($500–600)
   Version 2 – £250–300 ($400–500)
   Version 3 – £150–175 ($250–300)

M

Mistletoe Cottage
Annual Ornament

Mistletoe Cottage was the first in the series of annual Christmas Ornaments. Based upon a small tile-hung cottage in Kent, the model was intended to be used as a Christmas decoration.

Introduced in February 1992, Mistletoe Cottage was only available during that year before being retired in December 1992.

Produced: 1992
Height: 2½ in./6½ cm
Versions: 1
Backstamp: M
Current value: £15–20 ($30–35)

Moonlight Cove
English Collection – South-West

Situated on the estuary of the River Camel in Cornwall, this rugged fisherman's cottage still perpetuates the medieval arrangement of living quarters above, storage space below.

Introduced in February 1991, the model is still currently available.

Produced: 1991–
Height: 3¾ in./9½ cm
Versions: 1
Backstamp: L
Current value: £RRP ($RRP)

Moreton Manor

English Collection – Midlands

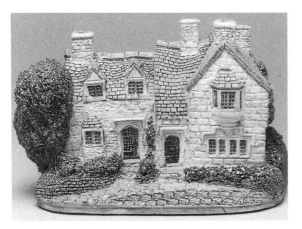

Built in the mid–1800s of local limestone, houses such as Moreton Manor can be found around the Cotswold villages of Lower and Upper Slaughter, Broadway and Moreton-in the-Marsh.

Introduced in February 1985, Moreton Manor was retired in December 1989.

Produced: 1985–89
Height: 3½ in./9 cm
Versions: 1
Backstamp: E
Current value: £65–75
   ($110–150)

M

Moselhaus

German Collection

In an area renowned for its wine, massive timber-framed houses and steeply terraced vineyards line the banks of the Moselle river.

Introduced in February 1987, Moselhaus is still currently available.

Produced: 1987–
Height: 5½ in./14 cm
Versions: 1
Backstamp: G
Current value: £RRP ($RRP)

Mrs Pinkerton's Post Office

English Collection − South-East

Based upon buildings to be found in East Anglia, Mrs Pinkerton's Post Office is built of flint cobbles, gathered from the surrounding fields or from the local beaches, complemented by local brick at the corners. A vital part of village life, Mrs Pinkerton's Post Office serves as a focal point for the community.

Introduced in November 1989, initially Mrs Pinkerton's Post Office was exclusively available from the UK Guild of Specialist China & Glass Retailers; however, after twelve months the model became generally available. Mrs Pinkerton's Post Office is still current.

Produced: 1989−
Height: 3¼ in./8 cm
Versions: 1
Backstamp: J
Current value: £RRP ($RRP)

Harvest Mill

*A recent introduction
to the American
Landmarks
collection and limited
to 3,500 pieces*

Honeysuckle
Cottage 1992

*Produced to
commemorate the
10th anniversary of
the launch of
Lilliput Lane; the
model was only
available in 1992*

The King's Arms

From the English Collection – South-East, introduced in 1990

Lighthouse

*From the
American Collection –
1st Series,
produced 1984–85*

Nürnberger Bürgerhaus

German Collection

Birthplace of the great painter and engraver Albrecht Dürer, Nuremberg is famed for its many historic buildings.

Introduced in February 1987, Nürnberger Bürgerhaus is still current.

Produced: 1987–
Height: 5-1/8 in./13 cm
Versions: 1
Backstamp: G
Current value: £RRP ($RRP)

The Nutshell

English Collection – South-East

Mersea Island, south of Colchester in Essex, is famous among small-boat sailors, and in the old town of West Mersea some attractive old fishing cottages still survive. The Nutshell can be found on Mersea Island; probably built in the mid-1800s, the timber-framed cottage has a half mansard roof to the front and weatherboarding on the walls.

Introduced in July 1992, The Nutshell is still currently available.

Produced: 1992–
Height: 2¾ in./7 cm
Versions: 1
Backstamp: M
Current value: £RRP ($RRP)

Oak Cottage

Blaise Hamlet Collection

One of the nine cottages based upon buildings at Blaise Hamlet, near Bristol, Oak Cottage, Circular Cottage and Diamond Cottage were the first three to be launched. One of only three thatched cottages in the Hamlet, Oak Cottage is built of Cotswold stone and features mullion windows.

Introduced in February 1989, Oak Cottage was retired in December 1993.

Produced: 1989–93
Height: 4½ in./11½ cm
Versions: 1

Backstamp: J
Current value: £50–60 ($150–175)

Oak Cottage

Classics Collection

One of the models in the miniature Classics Collection, Oak Cottage is a scaled down version of the cottage from the Blaise Hamlet Collection.

Introduced in February 1993, Oak Cottage is still current, although it is due to be retired in March 1995.

Produced: 1993–95
Height: 2-3/8 in./6 cm
Versions: 1
Backstamp: N
Current value: £RRP ($RRP)

Oak Lodge

English Collection – South-East

Oak Lodge is a typical example of a 16th-century Surrey farmhouse. Based upon a building to be found along the London–Portsmouth road, Oak Lodge has a timber frame infilled with brick (originally it would have been wattle and daub), and a clay tiled roof.

Introduced in September 1982, Oak Lodge was remodelled in September 1983. On the second version the roof tiles on the right-hand side were reduced from seven rows to five rows; the roof overhang on the left-hand side was reduced; and the timber framing was straightened. There was also a notice-able change around the base: version 2 has more foliage at the front and rear; the cobbles were more apparent; and the base was squared off.

Oak Lodge was retired in December 1987.

Produced: 1982–87
Height: 3 in./7½ cm
Versions: 2
Backstamp: A, D
Current value:
    Version 1 – £475–575 ($1,200–1,500)
    Version 2 – £70–90 ($175–225)

O

Oakwood Smithy

English Collection – South-East

The horseshoe-shaped entrance tells prospective customers that Oakwood Smithy is the home of the local blacksmith.

Introduced in February 1992, Oakwood Smithy is still current.

Produced: 1992–
Height: 4¾ in./12 cm
Versions: 1
Backstamp: M
Current value: £RRP ($RRP)

O'Lacey's Store

Irish Collection

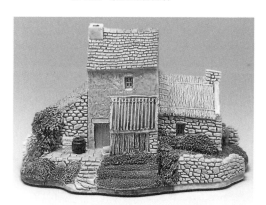

In County Mayo the village store is the place to catch up on what's happening – and buy the groceries. Originally a single-storey dwelling, as business grew so the second floor was added.

Introduced in July 1989, O'Lacey's Store is still current.

Produced: 1989–
Height: 3 in./7½ cm
Versions: 1
Backstamp: J
Current value: £RRP ($RRP)

The Old Curiosity Shop

English Collection – South-East

Situated in Portsmouth Street, in the famous 'Square Mile' of the City of London, The Old Curiosity Shop is a 16th-century antique shop which is reputed to have been the model for the book by Charles Dickens, who used to visit a friend near by.

Introduced in February 1985, the model was retired in December 1989.

Produced: 1985–89
Height: 3½ in./9 cm
Versions: 1
Backstamp: E
Current value: £80–100 ($125–150)

Old Mill

English Collection – South-West

Old Mill was the original version of Old Mine. Introduced in September 1982, it was soon realised that the model was a mine and not a mill; the model was quickly renamed Old Mine. It is believed that about 10 pieces were produced of Old Mill.

The illustrations show the model and its base, which was signed for the owner by David Tate at the 1993 Annual Fair.

Produced: 1982
Height: 3½ in./9 cm
Versions: 1 (*see also* Old Mine)
Backstamp: A
Current value: £3,000+ ($5,000+)

O

Old Mine

English Collection – South-West

Probably the most famous Lilliput Lane model, as well as also being rare.

Introduced in September 1982, Old Mine was decorated in a very distinct shade. The model was only in production for 10 months before being retired in July 1983. Only 200 pieces were produced, each with the original backstamp and the original label.

Produced: 1982–83
Height: 3½ in./9 cm
Versions: 1 (*see also* Old Mill)
Backstamp: A
Current value: £1,500–2,000
  ($3,000–4,000)

Old Mother Hubbard's

English Collection – South-West

Mother Hubbard's Cottage can be found in Yealmpton, in Devon. Legend has it that in 1804, Sarah Martin (whilst on holiday at the Kitley estate near Plymouth), wrote a lengthy rhyme about the housekeeper of the estate and called it 'Old Mother Hubbard'. When the housekeeper retired, she went to live in a cottage owned by the estate at Yealmpton; hence the cottage became known as 'Mother Hubbard's Cottage'.

Introduced in July 1993, Old Mother Hubbard's is still current.

Produced: 1993–
Height: 3-3/8 in./8½ cm
Versions: 1
Backstamp: N
Current value: £RRP
  ($RRP)

The Old Post Office
English Collection – South-West

The Old Post Office was one of the early Lilliput Lane models which was painted to resemble the stone houses of Oxfordshire, with soft yellow limestone and imported clay tiles.

Introduced in September 1982, The Old Post Office was retired in March 1986. However, the same mould was used in 1984 for Tintagel.

Produced: 1982–86
Height: 2¾ in./7 cm

Versions: 1
Backstamp: C, D
Current value: £300–350 ($650–750)

Old School House
English Collection – Northern

After Cliburn School had been retired in February 1984, the mould was then used for Old School House: as well as changing the name, Old School House was also painted in different colours.

Introduced in February 1984, the model was restyled during that year with the bell tower being thickened slightly.

Old School House was retired in December 1985.

Produced: 1984–85
Height: 2½ in./7 cm
Versions: 2
Backstamp: A, D
Current value:
   Version 1 – £500–600 ($1,250–1,500)
   Version 2 – £320–425 ($1,000–1,500)

O

Old Shop at Bignor

English Collection –
South-East

Close to the Weald and Downland Open Air Museum lies the village of Bignor, where the Old Shop is situated. A magnificent example of a 'Wealden' house, the Old Shop was built in the 15th century. Its oak frame is on a stone foundation, and the walls are made of wattle and daub with flint in-filling.

Introduced in July 1991, Old Shop at Bignor is still currently available, although it is due to be retired in March 1995.

Produced: 1991–95
Height: 4½ in./11½ cm
Versions: 1
Backstamp: L
Current value: £RRP ($RRP)

The Old Vicarage at Christmas

Christmas Specials

The fourth of the Christmas Specials, The Old Vicarage at Christmas depicts an enjoyable Christmas scene

Introduced in July 1991, the model was retired in February 1992.

Produced: 1991–92
Height: 4½ in./11½ cm
Versions: 1
Backstamp: L
Current value: £120–150 ($175–225)

Olde York Toll

Miscellaneous

Introduced in November 1989, although generally available world-wide, in the UK Olde York Toll was only retailed through Peter Jones China.

Olde York Toll was retired in December 1991.

Produced: 1989–91
Height: 4½ in./11½ cm
Versions: 1
Backstamp: J
Current value: £60–80
 ($100–125)

Orchard Farm Cottage

English Collection – South-East

Located close to the village of Hever in Kent, Orchard Farm Cottage was built in the late 17th century. It is classic vernacular architecture which makes good use of local materials. Timber framed on a stone plinth, some of the panels are of brick infill whilst others are weatherboarded in timber.

Introduced in February 1994, the model is still current.

Produced: 1994–
Height: 3¼ in./8 cm
Versions: 1
Backstamp: O
Current value: £RRP
 ($RRP)

O

Ostlers Keep

English Collection — South-West

Devon has the greatest concentration of earth-walled buildings, and the 'cob' cottage is characteristic of the area. Cob is a durable mixture of clay, straw and dung, which is usually laid on a stone foundation and then plastered with a clay and lime mixture.

Ostlers Keep is based upon a 16th century farmhouse which is now a public house. Introduced in February 1985, the cottage was retired in December 1991.

Produced: 1985–91
Height: 2¾ in./7 cm

Versions: 1
Backstamp: E
Current value: £60–80 ($85–110)

Otter Reach

English Collection — South-West

A cob cottage with a thick 'catslide' thatched roof, Otter Reach was introduced in July 1990; the model is still current.

Produced: 1990–
Height: 2-3/8 in./6 cm
Versions: 1
Backstamp: K
Current value: £RRP ($RRP)

Packhorse Bridge

Dealer Sign

Packhorse Bridge

Collectors Club

An accurate copy of a Lake District structure, Packhorse Bridge was originally produced as a dealer sign for use in the North American market.

Introduced in January 1985, the shield carried the wording 'Lilliput Lane Ltd', and in a scroll design underneath, the wording 'Parvus est Bellus' (which loosely translated means 'Small things are beautiful').

Retired in December 1985 for use as a dealer sign, Packhorse Bridge was then produced as a Collectors Club model in 1986.

Produced: 1985
Height: 1-3/8 in./3½ cm
Versions: 1
Backstamp: None used
Current value: £400–500 ($600–1,000)

When the Lilliput Lane Collectors Club was launched in March 1986, Packhorse Bridge was offered as the free gift to all members joining in that Club year, a tradition that still continues today.

Based upon a Lake District structure, this version of Packhorse Bridge differed from the North American dealer sign inasmuch as the shield carried the wording 'Official Collector Lilliput Lane', and the scroll design and wording underneath was omitted.

Packhorse Bridge was only offered during the Club year, which ran from March to February, so the model was retired in February 1987. In that first year, just under 5,000 people joined the Collectors Club.

Produced: 1986–87
Height: 1½ in./3½ cm
Versions: 1
Backstamp: None used
Current value: £275–350 ($500–600)

Paradise Lodge

English Collection –
Midlands

Based upon a lodge house situated in the grounds of Hodnet Hall, in Shropshire, Paradise Lodge is named after the surrounding area of Paradise Valley, which is a haven for all manner of flora and fauna.

Built in the 19th century using brick and stone, the lodge was originally occupied by the estate's gamekeeper.

Introduced in July 1991, Paradise Lodge is still current.

Produced: 1991–
Height: 4½ in./11½ cm
Versions: 1
Backstamp: L
Current value: £RRP ($RRP)

Pargetter's Retreat

English Collection – South-East

With its complex relief designs, this house could possibly be the home of a pargeter. Found mainly in the East Anglian region, pargeting was a method of creating relief plaster designs on the outside of a building, with each pargeter having his own recipe for the plaster.

Introduced in February 1988, Pargetter's Retreat was retired in December 1990.

Produced: 1988–90
Height: 4½ in./11½ cm
Versions: 1
Backstamp: H
Current value: £65–75
   ($80–100)

Partridge Cottage

Christmas Collection

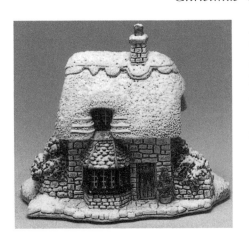

All of the miniature cottages in the Christmas Collection are intended to collectively set a lovely, wintery scene. Partridge Cottage conjures up thoughts of thick stone walls and roaring log fires.

Introduced in February 1993, the model is still current.

Produced: 1993–
Height: 2-3/8 in./6 cm
Versions: 1
Backstamp: N
Current value: £RRP ($RRP)

Pat Cohan's Bar

Irish Collection

The atmosphere of an Irish bar cannot be described – it has to be experienced. The bar bustles with activity as drinks are dispensed, racing bets are exchanged and business deals are struck, whilst at the same time the regulars are catching up on the latest gossip. And all of this goes on to the accompaniment of the local musicians playing the uilleann pipes, tin whistle, accordion and fiddle.

Introduced in July 1989, Pat Cohan's Bar is still currently available.

Produced: 1989–
Height: 3½ in./9 cm
Versions: 1
Backstamp: J
Current value: £RRP ($RRP)

Pear Tree House

English Collection – Midlands

Based upon a building in Herefordshire which is now used as the village post office, Pear Tree House was built in the 17th century of stone and timber and has an interesting dovecot gable.

Introduced in February 1991, Pear Tree House is still currently available.

Produced: 1991–
Height: 3¼ in./8 cm
Versions: 1
Backstamp: L
Current value: £RRP ($RRP)

Penny Lanes

Miscellaneous

Penny Lanes was a set of miniature models of town buildings, such as houses and shops. Produced in 1987, the models were never introduced into the retail market, hence there is very little information available about them. The models are not scaled-down versions of the Street Scenes buildings which were produced in the same year.

Due to the rarity of Penny Lanes, should any of the models come on to the secondary market they would certainly command a high premium.

Produced: 1987
Height: approx. 2 in./5 cm
Versions: Not known
Backstamp: Not known
Current value: £550+ each
($1,000+ each)

Penny Sweets

Village Shops Collection

Based upon a building situated in a Cotswold market town in Gloucestershire, Penny Sweets continued the Village Shops Collection theme of the traditional Cotswold stores. Built around 1700 using Cotswold stone and long-straw thatch, the house was converted into a sweet shop in 1865.

Introduced in July 1992, Penny Sweets is still currently available. (In the UK, the model was initially exclusive to the UK Guild of Specialist China & Glass Retailers before general release.)

Produced: 1992–
Height: 3½ in./9 cm
Versions: 1
Backstamp: M
Current value: £RRP ($RRP)

De Pepermolen

Netherlands Collection

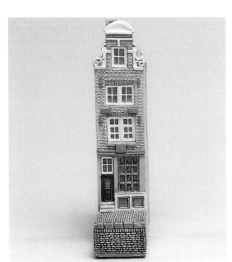

Since the time of the Dutch East India Company spices have been a valuable commodity, and the cellars of De Pepermolen (The Peppermill) would probably have contained the aromas of the various spices to remind the spice merchant of his wealth.

Introduced in February 1991, De Pepermolen (which is similar to Begijnhof apart from the colouring), is still currently available.

Produced: 1991–
Height: 4¾ in./12 cm
Versions: 1
Backstamp: L
Current value: £RRP ($RRP)

Pepsi Cola Barn

American Landmarks

Pepsi Cola Barn was introduced in March 1990, and after a relatively short production run it was retired in December 1991. This short production period has made it increasingly more difficult to acquire Pepsi Cola Barn on the secondary market.

Produced: 1990–91
Height: 3 in./7½ cm
Versions: 1
Backstamp: K
Current value: £120–160
($175–225)

Periwinkle Cottage

English Collection – South-West

Selworthy, on the fringe of Exmoor, is a picturesque village of well-tended, white-washed cottages preserved by the National Trust as part of the Holnicote Estate. The cottages, which are grouped around a communal green with interconnecting paths, were built in 1810 by the 10th Holnicote baronet, Sir Thomas Acland, as retirement homes for faithful retainers from the estate workforce.

Periwinkle Cottage is one of the most impressive cottages in the village.

Introduced in February 1990, Periwinkle Cottage is still currently available.

Produced: 1990–
Height: 4½ in./11 cm
Versions: 1
Backstamp: K
Current value: £RRP ($RRP)

Le Petit Montmartre
French Collection

A favourite haunt of artists and writers, Le Petit Montmartre (Little Montmartre) is a colourful area which the majority of visitors to Paris want to visit. For the numerous bistros and cafes offering food and drink on the terrace, it means opening early in the morning and closing very late at night.

Introduced in September 1990, Le Petit Montmartre is still currently available.

Produced: 1990–
Height: 5-1/8 in./13 cm
Versions: 1
Backstamp: K
Current value: £RRP ($RRP)

Petticoat Cottage

Collectors Club

Situated in Hampshire, on the edge of the New Forest, this cottage was built in the early 18th century. Using a stout timber frame within the brick walls, the cottage is topped with a decoratively gathered and swagged long-straw thatched roof.

Introduced in March 1994, Petticoat Cottage was offered to members who joined the Collectors Club during the twelve months from March 1994 to February 1995, at which time it was retired.

Produced: 1994–95
Height: 2½ in./6½ cm
Versions: 1
Backstamp: O
Current value: Not yet applicable

Pioneer Barn

American Landmarks

The smallest model in the American Landmarks collection, Pioneer Barn was introduced in March 1990.

As with Pepsi Cola Barn, Pioneer Barn was only in production for a short time before being retired in December 1991. Because of this, the model is dif-ficult to find on the secondary market.

Produced: 1990–91
Height: 1¾ in./4½ cm
Versions: 1
Backstamp: K
Current value: £50–95 ($75–100)

Pixie House

English Collection — South-West

At various locations throughout Cornwall unusual buildings can be found which bring back memories of the characters and dwellings described in *Grimms Fairy Tales* and other folklore. Pixie House conjures up visions of those green-clad, mischievous characters of Cornish folklore, the pixies.

Introduced in February 1992, Pixie House is still currently available.

Produced: 1992–
Height: 2¼ in./5½ cm
Versions: 1
Backstamp: M
Current value: £RRP ($RRP)

P

Ploughman's Cottage

Special Events

This 18th-century cottage can be found in the village of Nobottle, which is owned by the Althorp Estate, in Northamptonshire. Built from local stone and thatched with reed, the cottage was once the home of the estate manager.

Ploughman's Cottage was launched in September 1992 and was only available at Collectors Club events during the following twelve months until September 1993, when it was retired. Unlike its predecessors (Rowan Lodge and Gamekeeper's Cottage), this model was not pre-released in a different colourway at the South Bend Show, in response to collectors disapproval of this practice. The cottage could be personalised with the flowers painted in the member's choice of colours.

Produced: 1992–93
Height: 3 in./7½ cm
Versions: 1 (excluding personalised pieces)
Backstamp: M
Current value: £45–55 ($75–100)

La Porte Schoenenberg

French Collection

The Alsace region in France lies between the Vosges forest and Germany. An unusual region, to the tourist it appears to be more German than French. Based upon a gatehouse in the town of Riquewihr, which is famous for its excellent Riesling, La Porte Schoenenberg (Schoenenberg Gatehouse) dates from the 16th century.

Introduced in September 1990, La Porte Schoenenberg is still currently available.

Produced: 1990–
Height: 4 in./10 cm
Versions: 1
Backstamp: K
Current value: £RRP ($RRP)

Preston Mill
Scottish Collection

Preston Mill was based upon the oldest water-driven mill in Scotland. Built in the 16th century, the pantiled roof shows the thriving trade that existed between Scotland and the Low Countries in the 16th and 17th centuries.

Introduced in February 1985, the original version had stairs at the rear of the building, a barn door at the side and a short, pantiled roof.

In December 1986, it was extensively remodelled and the changes included: a water mill at the side of the building instead of the barn door; a tall, sectioned

pantiled roof; foliage at the rear of the building instead of stairs; and new style

Version 1, with a short, pantiled roof, a barn door at the side, and stairs at the rear

outbuildings. Besides these major changes, there were other minor alterations to detail.

Preston Mill was retired in July 1992.

Produced: 1985–92
Height: 3½ in./9 cm
Versions: 2
Backstamp: E, G
Current value:
　　Version 1 – £75–85 ($125–150)
　　Version 2 – £50–60 ($100–125)

Version 2, with a tall, sectioned pantiled roof, a water mill at the side instead of a barn door, foliage at the rear instead of stairs, and new style outbuildings

The Priest's House
English Collection – Northern

Standing opposite the churchyard in Prestbury, in Cheshire, The Priest's House is a magnificent example of Tudor half-timbered architecture in the 'magpie' style. Built in 1580, it is thought that the heavy framing timbers were used to support the weight of the stone roof, but as well as being functional the timbers were also decorative.

Introduced in July 1991, The Priest's House is still currently available, but is due to be retired in March 1995.

Produced: 1991–95
Height: 5-1/8 in./13 cm
Versions: 1
Backstamp: L
Current value: £RRP
　　($RRP)

Primrose Hill

English Collection – South-East

Puddlebrook

Collectors Club

Puddlebrook, a little thatched cottage, was offered as the free gift to members who joined the Lilliput Lane Collectors Club in the Club year beginning March 1991. Whereas other joining gifts had been non-cottage subjects, this was the first cottage to be offered.

Puddlebrook was retired at the close of the Club year in February 1992.

Produced: 1991–92
Height: 2½ in./6½ cm
Versions: 1
Backstamp: L
Current value: £50–60 ($50–75)

Typical of the 16th-century homes to be found in Chiddingstone, in Kent, the weatherboarding helped to protect the wattle and daub panels from the elements.

Introduced in February 1991, Primrose Hill is still currently available.

Produced: 1991–
Height: 3 in./7½ cm
Versions: 1
Backstamp: L
Current value: £RRP ($RRP)

Puffin Row

English Collection – South-West

On the north coast of Cornwall the only protected anchorage along a 40-mile stretch of inhospitable coastline is at Boscastle. Puffin Row is typical of the delightful white-washed cottages which greet the sailors when they enter Boscastle harbour.

Introduced in February 1992, Puffin Row is still currently available.

Produced: 1992–
Height: 3¼ in./8 cm
Versions: 1
Backstamp: M
Current value: £RRP
($RRP)

P

Purbeck Stores

English Collection – South-West

Nestling in the shadow of the ruins of Corfe Castle in Dorset, Purbeck Stores is a double bow-fronted cottage constructed from local stone. The roof, which also uses Purbeck stone, weighs around 1¼ tons per 100 square feet.

Introduced in February 1993, Purbeck Stores is still currently available.

Produced: 1993–
Height: 2½ in./6½ cm
Versions: 1
Backstamp: N
Current value: £RRP ($RRP)

Pussy Willow

Collectors Club

Pussy Willow was offered as the free gift to members who joined the Lilliput Lane Collectors Club during the Club year commencing March 1992. Only offered for a twelve-month period, Pussy Willow was retired in February 1993.

Produced: 1992–93
Height: 2½ in./6 cm
Versions: 1
Backstamp: M
Current value: £40–50 ($50–75)

Quiet Cottage
Irish Collection

When film director John Ford made his well-known film *The Quiet Man*, starring John Wayne and Maureen O'Hara, County Galway was the location he chose to 'shoot' the film. The cottage featured in the film was used by Lilliput Lane as the basis for Quiet Cottage.

Introduced in July 1989, Quiet Cottage was retired in December 1992.

Produced: 1989–92
Height: 2-3/8 in./6 cm
Versions: 1
Backstamp: J
Current value: £35–45 ($85–110)

Rambling Rose

American Landmarks

On the east coast of the USA, in the Massachusetts summer resort of Nantucket Island, the roses thrive in the blend of sunshine and fog that prevails on the island during the summer.

Introduced in June 1991, Rambling Rose is still currently available.

Produced: 1991–
Height: 2-3/8 in./6 cm
Versions: 1
Backstamp: L
Current value: £RRP ($RRP)

Das Rathaus

German Collection

Built in the 15th century and supported by stout oaken pillars, the town hall in Michelstadt is regarded as one of Germany's finest buildings.

Introduced in September 1988, Das Rathaus is still current.

Produced: 1988–
Height: 5½ in./14 cm
Versions: 1
Backstamp: H
Current value: £RRP ($RRP)

Red Lion Inn

English Collection – Northern

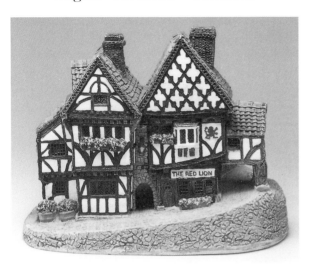

Red Lion Inn is based upon the architecture found in the city of York. Built from York stone, the roof uses pantiles (which originally came from Holland) and is part flagged at the rear of the building.

Introduced in September 1983, the model was retired in December 1987.

Produced: 1983–87
Height: 5¼ in./13½ cm
Versions: 1
Backstamp: C
Current value: £185–225
($325–400)

Rembrandt van Rijn

Netherlands Collection

The Dutch painter and graphic artist Rembrandt was the prodigious creator of over 600 paintings, about 300 etchings and nearly 2,000 drawings, many of which are regarded as masterpieces. The large house in Breestraat (now Jodenbreestraat), which he bought in 1639, and is depicted in Rembrandt van Rijn (Rembrandt's House), is now a museum. Introduced in February 1991, the model is still current.

Produced: 1991–
Height: 6 in./15 cm
Versions: 1
Backstamp: L
Current value: £RRP ($RRP)

Ring o' Bells
Christmas Collection

Another cottage in the miniature Christmas Collection, where the theme of the collection is a traditional village at Christmastime, Ring o' Bells shows the little country inn, built of Cotswold stone, which offers a warm welcome to locals and travellers alike.

Introduced in February 1994, this model is still current.

Produced: 1994–
Height: 2¾ in./7 cm
Versions: 1
Backstamp: O
Current value: £RRP ($RRP)

The Rising Sun
English Collection – South-East

The Rising Sun, a small thatched public house, is situated in the village of Ickford, near Thame. The upper parts are timber framed which have then been infilled with wichert.

Introduced in September 1988, The Rising Sun was retired in July 1992.

Produced: 1988–92
Height: 2¼ in./6 cm
Versions: 1
Backstamp: H
Current value: £50–60 ($80–100)

Riverside Chapel

American Landmarks

With the opening up of the American Mid-west, the early settlers included European migrants who were searching for religious and political freedom. As religion was such an important part of the settlers life, a church or chapel was one of the first community buildings to be erected.

Riverside Chapel was introduced in March 1990, and was retired in December 1993.

Produced: 1990–93
Height: 3½ in./9 cm
Versions: 1
Backstamp: K
Current value: £60–70
　　　($125–150)

R

Riverview

English Collection – Midlands

This tiny cottage is situated just north of Welshpool on the border of England and Wales. Backing on to a tributary of the River Severn, the timber-framed cottage has retained its 'magpie' look on the southern front, but other than the addition of mains water and electricity the cottage is much the same as when it was originally built.

Introduced in July 1987, it is thought that on pieces produced before 1989 the rocks around the cottage were painted grey, whereas from 1989 onwards they were painted white.

Riverview was retired in July 1994.

Produced: 1987–94
Height: 2 in./5 cm
Versions: 2
Backstamp: G
Current value:
Version 1 – £25–35 ($45–55)
Version 2 – £20–25 ($40–50)

Roadside Coolers

American Landmarks

At the heart of every American small town was the General Store, and on hot, summer days the locals would come in search of refreshment. The store depicted in Roadside Coolers – with its stack of water melons outside – was ready and waiting.

Introduced in March 1990, Roadside Coolers was retired in July 1994.

Produced: 1990–94
Height: 3 in./7½ cm
Versions: 1
Backstamp: K
Current value: £65–70 ($100–125)

Robin Cottage

Annual Ornament

The second in the series of Annual Ornaments intended for use as Christmas decorations, Robin Cottage was introduced in February 1993. Only available during that year, Robin Cottage was retired in December 1993.

Produced: 1993
Height: 2½ in./6 cm
Versions: 1
Backstamp: N
Current value: £20–25 ($30–40)

Robins Gate

English Collection – Midlands

This picturesque 19th-century gatehouse was the only cottage introduced into the English Collection – Midlands in July 1990. Robins Gate is still currently available.

Produced: 1990–
Height: 2-3/8 in./6 cm
Versions: 1
Backstamp: K
Current value: £RRP ($RRP)

Rose Cottage

English Collection – South-West

Situated in Blaise Hamlet (which has provided the subjects for a number of Lilliput Lane cottages), Rose Cottage was designed by the architects John Nash and George Repton. Built around 1810, the cottage featured a Cotswold split stone double roof, with brick-built chimney stacks; Nash and Repton used specially moulded materials for much of the brickwork.

Introduced in February 1991, Rose Cottage is still currently available.

Produced: 1991–
Height: 4½ in./11½ cm
Versions: 1
Backstamp: L
Current value: £RRP ($RRP)

R

Rose Cottage

Classics Collection

As with the other models in this collection, Rose Cottage originates in Blaise Hamlet. Designed by John Nash and George Repton, Nash said that Blaise Hamlet imparted more pleasure than anything he had ever planned.

Introduced in February 1993, Rose Cottage is still current, although it is due to be retired in March 1995.

Produced: 1993–95
Height: 2-3/8 in./6 cm
Versions: 1
Backstamp: N
Current value: £RRP ($RRP)

Rose Cottage, Skirsgill

Special

Built in 1760, Rose Cottage is within the Lilliput Lane Visitors Centre at Skirsgill, near Penrith, where the model of the cottage can be purchased by personal callers.

Introduced in August 1991, after 200 pieces were produced the mould was changed and a dog added on the right-hand side. The cottage was later restyled to reflect the actual building itself, including the change of the right-hand chimney from render to brick. This third version is still current.

Produced: 1991–
Height: 3 in./7½ cm
Versions: 3
Backstamp: L, O
Current value:
    Version 1 – £400+ ($700+)
    Version 2 – £80–110 ($250–300)
    Version 3 – £50–60 ($150–175)

Detail of the side of the original version of Rose Cottage (left), and the second version with the dog (right)

160

Mail Pouch Barn

*From the American Landmarks
collection, produced 1989–93*

Midwest Barn

*From the American Collection – 1st Series,
produced 1984–85*

San Francisco House

From the American Collection – 1st Series; produced 1984–85 in two colourways

Seven Dwarfs Cottage

An exclusive model for Disney World in the USA, produced 1986

Rosengartenhaus

German Collection

Rosengarten is a suburb of Hamburg (one of Germany's largest cities), and Rosengartenhaus (Rosegarden House) is typical of the buildings to be found in the area.

The timber-framed house, which has been converted from two barns, features an interesting piece of local legend. Homes in this area usually have two carved horses heads, either on the roof or on the gables. Believed to ward off bad luck, it is also said that if the heads point inwards then the daughter of the house is betrothed, if they point outwards, then she is still single.

Introduced in February 1992, Rosengartenhaus is still currently available.

Produced: 1992–
Height: 2¾ in./7 cm
Versions: 1
Backstamp: J
Current value: £RRP ($RRP)

Rowan Lodge

Special Events

Rowan Lodge was introduced in September 1990 at the South Bend Show in the USA, when 350 pieces were produced each stamped SOUTH BEND 90.

A second version was then produced and made available at Collectors Club events. This version had the roof in a different colour, and it was possible for members to have the door painted in the colour of their choice.

Only available for one year after its introduction, Rowan Lodge was retired in September 1991.

Produced: 1990–91
Height: 3½ in./9 cm
Versions: 2 (excluding personalised pieces)
Backstamp: K
Current value:
   Version 1 – £300–400 ($350–400)
   Version 2 – £70–100 ($100–150)

R

The Royal Oak

English Collection – South-West

Based upon an inn to be found on Exmoor, this 12th-century building has smooth clay cob walls and Devon thatch.

Introduced in September 1988, The Royal Oak was retired in December 1991.

Produced: 1988–91
Height: 4¼ in./11 cm
Versions: 1
Backstamp: G
Current value: £90–120 ($175–200)

Rozengracht

Netherlands Collection

Built in the 17th century, Rozengracht (Rose Canal) can be found in the Jordaan area of Amsterdam. A modest but attractive house, its bow window and small stepped gable are typical of the district.

Introduced in February 1991, Rozengracht is still currently available. Unlike the majority of the models in the Netherlands Collection, this mould has not been used to produce another model with different colouring.

Produced: 1991–
Height: 4¼ in./11 cm
Versions: 1
Backstamp: L
Current value: £RRP ($RRP)

Runswick House

English Collection – Northern

Rustic Root House

English Collection – Midlands

Runswick House typifies east Yorkshire vernacular architecture with its sturdy stone walls and pantile roof.

Introduced in July 1990, Runswick House is still currently available.

Produced: 1990–
Height: 3¼ in./8 cm
Versions: 1
Backstamp: K
Current value: £RRP ($RRP)

Close to – but at the same time a discreet distance from – the main road leading to the Duke of Beaufort's estate at Badminton with its impressive Palladian mansion, is an 18th-century almshouse. Designed by Thomas Wright, Rustic Root House is a thatched cottage which looks somewhat like an upturned boat. It is situated in an attractive hamlet which predates Blaise Hamlet by about 60 years.

Introduced in February 1992, Rustic Root House is still currently available.

Produced: 1992–
Height: 3¼ in./8 cm
Versions: 1
Backstamp: M
Current value: £RRP ($RRP)

R

Rydal View

English Collection — Northern

Rydal View is typical of the white-washed houses which stand out against the green of the Lakeland countryside.

Built around 300 years ago and using local grey/green slate with a split slate roof and round slate chimneys, the walls have been rendered with cement and then whitewashed.

Introduced in February 1987, Rydal View was retired in December 1989.

Produced: 1987–89
Height: 5¼ in./13½ cm
Versions: 1
Backstamp: G
Current value: £100–140 ($225–250)

Saddler's Inn

English Collection – Midlands

Typical of the Staffordshire area because of the timber framing and the size of the panelling, this 17th century building was originally an inn. At one time it would have had a thatched roof, and there would have been some stables, but these have long since gone.

Introduced in February 1987, Saddler's Inn was retired in December 1989.

Produced: 1987–89
Height: 3 in./7½ cm
Versions: 1
Backstamp: G
Current value: £40–60 ($80–100)

Saffron House

English Collection – South-East

Saffron Walden in Essex is an unspoilt small town with superb medieval buildings. The town's wealth came from wool and from the saffron crop, which was a medicine as well as a dye.

Saffron House is based upon a Victorian hunting lodge which has some unusual features, particularly the ornate gables. Introduced in February 1994, the model is still current.

Produced: 1994–
Height: 4¼ in./11 cm
Versions: 1
Backstamp: O
Current value: £RRP ($RRP)

S

San Francisco House

American Collection – 1st Series

This typical San Francisco House was introduced in October 1984. Produced in two colourways, the first (which is the rarer of the two) has pink walls, white windows and a brown door, whereas the second version has yellow walls, white window frames, blue decoration above and below the first floor windows, and blue decoration over a blue door.

When San Francisco House was retired in October 1985, 400 pieces had been produced.

Produced: 1984–85
Height: 4¼ in./10¾ cm
Versions: 2
Backstamp: D
Current value: Version 1 – £475–550 ($750–1,000)
   Version 2 – £275–300 ($350–450)

Sawrey Gill

English Collection – Northern

The writer Beatrix Potter lived at Hill Top Farm in Near Sawrey on the west side of Windermere; her first book *The Tale of Peter Rabbit* was published in 1902, not long after she moved to Lakeland. When she died in 1943 she bequeathed her house and much of the surrounding land to the National Trust.

Introduced in July 1985, Sawrey Gill was the Lilliput Lane interpretation of Beatrix Potter's house; the model was retired in July 1992.

Produced: 1985–92
Height: 2½ in./5¾ cm
Versions: 1
Backstamp: E
Current value: £30–40 ($45–55)

Saxham St Edmunds

English Collection – South-East (Limited Edition)

Suffolk is a county with many interesting old buildings to be found in its towns and villages. Saxham St Edmunds was the Lilliput Lane interpretation of a traditional Suffolk village, its name being derived from the Saxon king of the region, Edmund.

The distinctive thing about the village was the colour of the thatched cottages; the plaster was coloured, using elderberries or ox blood, to give all of the cottages a distinctive hue known as 'Suffolk Pink'.

Introduced in July 1991, Saxham St Edmunds was due to be produced in a limited edition of 4,500 pieces, with priority being given for the first six months to members of the Collectors Club. However, Saxham St Edmunds was retired in December 1994, before being fully subscribed; the number of pieces produced is due to be announced later.

Produced: 1991–94
Height: 6 in./15 cm
Versions: 1
Backstamp: L
Current value: £RRP ($RRP)

S

Saxon Cottage

English Collection — South-East

Saxon Cottage, in Steyning in East Sussex, is currently owned by the National Trust; it was built in the 15th century and was once part of a much larger building. Oak framed with panels of split oak, laths and plaster, the cottage has a magnificent thatched catslide roof.

Introduced in February 1988, Saxon Cottage was retired in December 1989.

Produced: 1988–89
Height: 5½ in./13¾ cm
Versions: 1
Backstamp: H
Current value: £120–150 ($225–275)

School Days

American Landmarks

In 19th-century America the school house was a simple one-roomed building. But however simple the building, it was still possible to teach the pupils the three Rs and basic discipline.

Introduced in June 1991, School Days is still currently available.

Produced: 1991–
Height: 2¾ in./7 cm
Versions: 1
Backstamp: L
Current value: £RRP ($RRP)

Schwarzwaldhaus

German Collection

Based upon the buildings to be found in the Black Forest, the immediately noticeable feature of Schwarzwaldhaus is the roof. The large overhanging roof is designed to protect the windows, doors and verandah from the massive snowfalls which occur in this region in winter.

Introduced in February 1987, the model is still currently available.

Produced: 1987–
Height: 4¼ in./11 cm
Versions: 1
Backstamp: M
Current value: £RRP ($RRP)

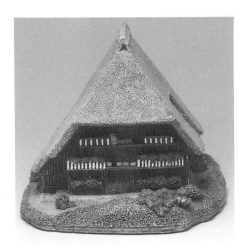

Scroll on the Wall

Miscellaneous

Scroll on the Wall shows the Lilliputians unfurling a banner which has the wording 'Lilliput Lane' upon it. Introduced in February 1986, the model was retired in December 1987.

Produced: 1986–87
Height: 3¼ in./8 cm
Versions: 1
Backstamp: F
Current value: £150–200 ($225–300)

S

Secret Garden

English Collection – Northern

From the way in which the garden paths and statuary have fallen into disrepair and the rampant growth of the plants been left unchecked, it seems that this Victorian Gothic house has been left unoccupied for a long time.

Introduced in February 1987, Secret Garden was retired in July 1994.

Produced: 1987–94
Height: 5½ in./14 cm
Versions: 1
Backstamp: G
Current value: £70–75
   ($225–250)

See Rock City

American Landmarks

This wooden building at the top of Lookout Mountain is a marvellous vantage point which, as well as giving you a good view of Rock City, also enables you to see seven of the American states on a clear day.

Introduced in June 1993, See Rock City is still currently available.

Produced: 1993–
Height: 2¾ in./7 cm
Versions: 1
Backstamp: N
Current value: £RRP ($RRP)

Settler's Surprise

Exclusive

Settler's Surprise was based upon Sod Cottage, an early New Zealand settler's dwelling which has been rebuilt at Howick Colonial Village Museum near Auckland. The Museum is run by Howick & District's Historical Society and is open to the public.

Introduced in October 1991, Settler's Surprise was produced exclusively for the New Zealand market; the model is still currently available in New Zealand.

Produced: 1991–
Height: 2¼ in./5½ cm
Versions: 1
Backstamp: L
Current value: £60–80 ($195–225)

Seven Dwarfs Cottage

Exclusive

Seven Dwarfs Cottage was produced exclusively for Disney World in the USA. Introduced in February 1986, 470 pieces were produced before the model was retired in December 1986.

Produced: 1986
Height: 5¼ in./13 cm
Versions: 1
Backstamp: None used
Current value: £700–900 ($300–450)

7 St Andrews Square

Scottish Collection

Culross, in Fife, is a town of 16th- and 17th-century red-tiled houses lining steep cobbled streets, which has been splendidly preserved by the National Trust for Scotland.

7 St Andrews Square is a typical house from the region; built from yellow sandstone and roofed with tiles imported from the Low Countries, an interesting feature is the external stair.

Introduced in July 1985, the model was retired in December 1986.

Produced: 1985–86
Height: 2¼ in./5½ cm
Versions: 1
Backstamp: E
Current value: £80–120 ($125–150)

Shave and a Haircut

American Landmarks

Shave and a Haircut takes you back to the days when, as well as being able to get a shave and a haircut, you could also be serenaded by the barber shop quartet.

Introduced in June 1993, the model is still currently available.

Produced: 1993–
Height: 3 in./7½ cm
Versions: 1
Backstamp: N
Current value: £RRP ($RRP)

Ship Inn

English Collection – Northern

Based upon the many similar buildings to be found in York, the Ship Inn has exposed timber framing, magnificent Tudor chimneys and pantiles (which were originally imported from Holland).

Introduced in February 1988, Ship Inn was retired in July 1992.

Produced: 1988–92
Height: 5¾ in./14½ cm
Versions: 1
Backstamp: H
Current value: £130–150 ($250–275)

Sign of the Times

American Landmarks

Sign of the Times recalls the early days of motoring in America when billboards were positioned alongside the two-lane roads, long before the advent of highways and interstates.

Introduced in March 1990, the model is still currently available.

Produced: 1990–
Height: 2¼ in./5½ cm
Versions: 1
Backstamp: K
Current value: £RRP ($RRP)

Simply Amish

American Landmarks

A conservative Protestant sect which is well established in America, the Amish advocate strict community conformity. They are self-sufficient so farming is of major importance to them. Simply Amish shows a typical barn used for storage. The film *Witness*, starring Harrison Ford, which was set amongst an Amish community, gave an insight into their culture.

Introduced in January 1993, the model was only available in the USA during that year; it is now available world-wide.

Produced: 1993–
Height: 4 in./10 cm
Versions: 1
Backstamp: N
Current value: £RRP ($RRP)

16.9 Cents per Gallon

American Landmarks

With the advent of the motor car, many general stores began to sell fuel; in those early days a gallon was a lot cheaper than today!

Introduced in June 1992, the model is still currently available.

Produced: 1992–
Height: 3 in./7½ cm
Versions: 1
Backstamp: M
Current value: £RRP ($RRP)

Small Town Library

American Landmarks

The Smallest Inn

English Collection – South-West

Together with the church and chapel, the library was another building which was erected for the benefit of the community.

Introduced in January 1992, Small Town Library is still currently available.

Produced: 1992–
Height: 4 in./10 cm
Versions: 1
Backstamp: M
Current value: £RRP ($RRP)

There are a number of public houses in England which lay claim to be the smallest in the country, and the one upon which this Lilliput Lane model is based can be found in Dorset.

Built in the 15th century, this thatched inn is reputed to have been a blacksmith's shop until King Charles II stopped to have his horse shod and asked for a drink. When the blacksmith told the King that he had no licence to serve drink, the King granted him one there and then.

Introduced in September 1988, The Smallest Inn was retired in December 1991.

Produced: 1988–91
Height: 2¼ in./6 cm
Versions: 1
Backstamp: H
Current value: £40–60 ($50–75)

S

Snowdon Lodge

Christmas Lodge Collection

The third in the series of four Christmas lodges, Snowdon Lodge was based upon the granite lodge at the entrance to the estate of the Williams-Ellis family at Garreg, near Portmeirion in Wales.

Introduced in February 1994, Snowdon Lodge was only available during that year and was retired in December 1994.

Produced: 1994
Height: 4¼ in./11 cm
Versions: 1
Backstamp: O
Current value: £RRP ($RRP)

The Spinney

Collectors Club

This 18th-century farmworker's cottage with later Victorian additions was offered as the free gift to members who joined the Lilliput Lane Collectors Club in the Club year beginning March 1993.

The Spinney was retired at the close of the Club year in February 1994.

Produced: 1993–94
Height: 2½ in./6½ cm
Versions: 1
Backstamp: N
Current value: £20–30 ($50–75)

Spring Bank

English Collection — South-West

Many timber-framed thatched cottages are to be found around the Lyme Regis area of Dorset, and most of them date back many centuries.

Spring Bank was introduced in February 1986 and was retired in December 1991.

Produced: 1986–91
Height: 2½ in./6½ cm
Versions: 1
Backstamp: F
Current value: £45–55 ($75–100)

Spring Gate Cottage

English Collection — South-West

S

The picturesque village of Luccombe, in Somerset, is part of the Holnicote Estate and is owned by the National Trust. Spring Gate Cottage, which can be found in the village, was built in the early 17th century and shows a wide diversity of style and material used in the design and construction.

Introduced in July 1994, Spring Gate Cottage is still currently available.

Produced: 1994–
Height: 4 in./10 cm
Versions: 1
Backstamp: O
Current value: £RRP ($RRP)

Spring Glory

A Year in an English Garden

Due to be launched in February 1995, Spring Glory is one of the four cottages in the series which shows how each season affects the appearance of a cottage. The seasonal portrayals are: spring (Spring Glory), summer (Summer Impressions), autumn (Autumn Hues) and winter (Winter's Wonder). Autumn Hues and Winter's Wonder were released in 1994, with the remaining two cottages being released in 1995.

Produced: 1995–
Height: 3-3/8 in./8½ cm
Versions: 1
Backstamp: P
Current value: £RRP ($RRP)

St Columba's School

Irish Collection

St Columba's School is typical of the small Irish school where the local people would have received their early education, some of them possibly going on to become scholars, writers and poets.

Introduced in July 1989, the model is still current.

Produced: 1989–
Height: 2-3/8 in./6 cm
Versions: 1
Backstamp: J
Current value: £RRP ($RRP)

St Govan's Chapel

Welsh Collection

Situated at St Govan's Head in Pembrokeshire, St Govan's Chapel measures only 20 ft by 12 ft (6 m by 3½ m), and is perched halfway down the cliffs and approached by a steep flight of steps. The chapel dates from the 13th century, but the altar and seat were cut into the stone much earlier.

Introduced in July 1992, St Govan's Chapel is still current.

Produced: 1992–
Height: 2½ in./6 cm
Versions: 1
Backstamp: M
Current value: £RRP ($RRP)

St Joseph's Church

Christmas Collection

The Christmas Collection is a series of miniature cottages and buildings. With the theme of a traditional wintery village scene at Christmastime, St Joseph's Church prepares for the villagers attending midnight Mass.

Introduced in February 1993, St Joseph's Church is still current.

Produced: 1993–
Height: 3½ in./9 cm
Versions: 1
Backstamp: N
Current value: £RRP ($RRP)

S

St Joseph's School

Christmas Collection

Another building in the miniature Christmas Collection, St Joseph's School is based upon a similar building at Eastcombe, near Stroud in Gloucestershire. This Victorian school-house, which was built in 1878, has separate entrances for boys and girls.

Introduced in February 1994, St Joseph's School is still current.

Produced: 1994–
Height: 2¾ in./7 cm
Versions: 1
Backstamp: O
Current value: £RRP ($RRP)

St Kevin's Church

Irish Collection

Situated in County Wicklow, St Kevin's Church is one of the most important ancient ecclesiastical buildings in Ireland. The church is named after St Kevin, who was a 7th-century hermit who lived in a tiny cell near by and devoted his time and energy to a simple religious life.

Introduced in July 1989, St Kevin's Church is still current.

Produced: 1989–
Height: 4 in./10 cm
Versions: 1
Backstamp: J
Current value: £RRP ($RRP)

St Lawrence Church
English Collection – Northern

The Church of St Lawrence can be found in Crosby Ravensworth, Cumbria. Built in the 12th century and encircled by old trees, it is one of the finest churches in east Cumbria and is like a miniature cathedral in appearance.

Introduced in July 1989, St Lawrence Church is still current.

Produced: 1989–
Height: 5 in./12½ cm
Versions: 1
Backstamp: J
Current value: £RRP ($RRP)

St Marks
English Collection – Midlands

Based upon Kington Church which is in Hereford and Worcester, St Marks depicts a timber-framed church which was built in the 15th/16th century, but does

have features which suggest that it could be as old as the 14th century.

Introduced in February 1988, St Marks was retired in December 1991.

Produced: 1988–91
Height: 3¾ in./9½ cm
Versions: 1
Backstamp: H
Current value: £60–80
($100–125)

S

St Mary's Church
English Collection – Midlands

St Mary's Church depicts the classic English church which is to be found in so many towns and villages, and has been built from a variety of stone and slate.

Introduced in February 1985, St Mary's Church was retired in December 1988.

Produced: 1985–88
Height: 3¾ in./9½ cm
Versions: 1
Backstamp: E
Current value: £70–100
($100–125)

St Mary's Church
Studley Royal Collection (Limited Edition)

Built by the Marchioness of Ripon in 1871–78, St Mary's Church was designed by the architect William Burges. Situated at the west end of the main avenue at Studley Royal in Yorkshire, the Church is owned by the Church of England and maintained by the Historic Buildings and Monuments Commission, but shown by the National Trust.

Not to be confused with St Mary's Church from the English Collection – Midlands, this model was introduced in July 1994 exclusively in the USA, in a limited edition of 5,000 pieces. At present St Mary's Church is only available in the USA, although it is anticipated that the model will be generally released in 1995.

Produced: 1994–

Height: 6 in./15 cm
Versions: 1
Backstamp: O
Current value: £Not known ($RRP)

St Nicholas Church

Christmas Specials

Based upon a church in southern Lakeland not far from Penrith, St Nicholas Church was the second model in the Christmas Specials.

Introduced in October 1989, it was retired in February 1990.

Produced: 1989–90
Height: 4 in./10 cm
Versions: 1
Backstamp: J
Current value: £110–140
   ($175–225)

St Patrick's Church

Irish Collection

In Ireland the Roman Catholic Church plays a significant role in the lives of the people and also in the country, and churches such as St Patrick's (together with the parish priest or minister) are vital to the well-being of the community.

Introduced in July 1989, St Patrick's Church was retired in July 1993.

Produced: 1989–93
Height: 6-3/8 in./16 cm
Versions: 1
Backstamp: J
Current value: £80–90
   ($200–225)

S

St Peter's Cove
English Collection – South-East (Limited Edition)

St Peter's Cove was the Lilliput Lane interpretation of a southern England village. The dwellings depicted in the sculpture were based upon buildings to be found in the Isle of Wight at Godshill and Ventnor, together with other buildings from the Meon Valley in Hampshire and the New Forest around Christchurch in Dorset. There were nine individual buildings on the sculpture including a church, thatched and brick-built cottages.

Introduced in February 1989 and limited to 3,000 pieces, St Peter's Cove was fully subscribed within six months. However, because of the complexity of the sculpture and its lengthy production time, it took almost two years for the orders to be fulfilled, at which time St Peter's Cove was officially retired (in December 1991).

Produced: 1989–91
Height: 8 in./20 cm
Versions: 1
Backstamp: J
Current value: £800–1,100
   ($1,800–2,200)

Stocklebeck Mill

English Collection – Northern

Stocklebeck Mill depicts a 19th-century watermill in Cumbria and features the typical building materials of that time. The sculpture was created by Lilliput Lane from descriptions and old drawings.

Introduced in February 1993, the model is still currently available.

Produced: 1993–
Height: 4¾ in./12 cm
Versions: 1
Backstamp: N
Current value: £RRP ($RRP)

Stockwell Tenement

Scottish Collection

When Stockwell Tenement was built, the word 'tenement' was used to refer to a room or set of rooms within a house, whereas today people associate it more with blocks of high-rise flats.

Introduced in July 1989, Stockwell Tenement is still currently available.

Produced: 1989–
Height: 4¼ in./11 cm
Versions: 1
Backstamp: J
Current value: £RRP ($RRP)

S

Stokesay

Historical Castles of England – Midlands

Stokesay, south of Craven Arms in Shropshire, is a perfectly preserved 13th-century fortified stone manor, which consists of two sturdy stone towers joined by a great gabled banqueting hall with tall Gothic windows. The 'black-and-white' Elizabethan gatehouse has a stone roof and an overhanging upper storey.

Introduced in July 1994, Stokesay is still current.

Produced: 1994–
Height: 3-3/8 in./8½ cm
Versions: 1
Backstamp: O
Current value: £RRP ($RRP)

Stone Cottage
English Collection — South-East

One of the first models produced by Lilliput Lane, Stone Cottage was introduced in September 1982.

The original version, which carried backstamp A, had the name of the cottage embossed on the front of the base, each of the main windows at the front had eighteen panes, the chimney pots were short, the roofline was straight, the grass area to the left front measured approximately 2–3 cm, and the base was small and cut.

The model was altered in September 1983 when the name was removed from the front of the base; this second version carried either backstamp A or C.

A third version then brought further changes: the roofline was given a distinctive sagging, the number of window panes was reduced to twelve, and the base became about one-third larger with more of a finished look. This version carried backstamp D.

A fourth version was then produced around September 1986, when the chimneys were made taller; again this version carried backstamp D.

Stone Cottage was retired in December 1986.

Produced: 1982–86
Height: 3¾ in./9½ cm
Versions: 4
Backstamp: A, C, D
Current value:
  Version 1 – £425–475 ($650–750)
  Version 2 – £300–350 ($450–500)
  Version 3 – £175–200 ($300–400)
  Version 4 – £225–275 ($400–500)

[A piece has been found which suggests that yet another version was produced of Stone Cottage. This piece is similar to version 2 but the roof has ten ridge tiles instead of five/six, the base is larger, and the chimneys are taller. As the piece lacks any backstamp or label no accurate dating can be made.]

S

Stone Cottage: version 4 (left), and version 2 (right)

Stoneybeck

English Collection – Northern

Built over 200 years ago of local stone with a split slate roof, Stoneybeck is a typical Cumbrian whitewashed cottage, and examples can be seen dotted all over the Lake District.

Introduced in February 1987, Stoneybeck was retired in July 1992.

Produced: 1987–92
Height: 2¾ in./7 cm
Versions: 1
Backstamp: G
Current value: £40–45 ($65–85)

Stradling Priory

English Collection – South-West

Built in 1836 by William Stradling, supposedly on the site of a Benedictine monastery near Glastonbury, Somerset, his intention was to create a museum of artefacts and curiosities from the area. Over the years a variety of objects were accumulated, but in 1938 many of them were taken and never returned. The building is now a private property.

Introduced in February 1993, Stradling Priory is still current.

Produced: 1993–
Height: 4¼ in./11 cm
Versions: 1
Backstamp: N
Current value: £RRP ($RRP)

Strandvogthaus

German Collection

Strandvogthaus (Beach Warden's House) originates from the Frisian island of Sylt in northern Germany. Originally built in 1699 by a sea captain called Lorens Petersen de Hahn, the house has now been moved and rebuilt at the Schleswig-Holstein Open Air Museum near Kiel.

Introduced in February 1992,

Strandvogthaus is still currently available.

Produced: 1992–
Height: 2¾ in./7 cm
Versions: 1
Backstamp: M
Current value: £RRP ($RRP)

Strawberry Cottage

English Collection – South-East

Built in the 15th century, Strawberry Cottage can be found in East Sussex. Originally the home of a tinker, the cottage is half timbered with oak beams and wattle and daub infill. Thatched with reed from the nearby Romney Marsh, the roof has a catslide on one side.

Introduced in February 1990, Strawberry Cottage is still currently available.

Produced: 1990–
Height: 2½ in./6½ cm
Versions: 1
Backstamp: J
Current value: £RRP ($RRP)

S

Street Scenes 1–10
Miscellaneous

Street Scenes (from left): models 1, 2, 3, 4 and 5

The ten models which make up the Street Scenes collection were introduced in February 1987. Each model had the company name impressed on the rear, together with a number (from 1 to 10), but other than this there was no other means of identification.

The collection was only produced for ten months and was retired in December 1987. (*See also* Penny Lanes.)

Produced: 1987
Height: 6–7 in./15–17½ cm
Versions: 1
Backstamp: G
Current value:
No. 1–3 £120–150 each ($200–250 each)
No. 4–10 £75–100 each ($150–200 each)

Street Scenes (from left): models 6, 7, 8, 9 and 10

Sulgrave Manor

English Collection — Midlands

Sulgrave Manor in Northamptonshire is a compact, two-storey 16th century manor house. The American flag flies over the building because it was built in 1560 by Lawrence Washington, an ancestor of George Washington, whose coat and saddlebags are on display inside. The Washington family coat of arms, which is over the porch and consists of two bars and three stars, is thought to have been the basis for the Stars and Stripes. The manor house is now a museum.

Introduced in February 1990, Sulgrave Manor was retired in December 1992.

Produced: 1990–92
Height: 3¾ in./9½ cm
Versions: 1
Backstamp: K
Current value: £70–100 ($125–175)

S

Summer Haze

English Collection – Midlands

Built almost 400 years ago, this small, cruck-framed, thatched cottage can be found in Oxfordshire.

Introduced in February 1987, Summer Haze was retired in July 1993.

Produced: 1987–93
Height: 4 in./10 cm
Versions: 1
Backstamp: G
Current value: £55–60 ($125–150)

Summer Impressions

A Year in an English Garden

Due to be launched in February 1995, together with Spring Glory, Summer Impressions is one of the four cottages in the series which shows how each season affects the appearance of a cottage. The seasonal portrayals are: spring (Spring Glory), summer (Summer Impressions), autumn (Autumn Hues) and winter (Winter's Wonder). Autumn Hues and Winter's Wonder were released in 1994, with the remaining two cottages being released in 1995.

Produced: 1995–
Height: 3-3/8 in./8½ cm
Versions: 1
Backstamp: P
Current value: £RRP ($RRP)

St Peter's Cove

*From the English Collection − South-East and limited to 3,000 pieces,
it was fully subscribed within six months of its introduction in February 1989.
The illustration below shows some of the fine detail of the model*

Stone Cottage

From the English Collection – South-East and produced 1982–86, it is possible that five versions were made. The illustration above shows the front view of versions 2 (left) and 4 (right); the illustration below shows the rear view of version 2 (left) and a recently discovered piece (possibly version 5)

Sunnyside

English Collection – South-East

Sunnyside is situated in Hampshire not far from the village of Selborne, the birthplace and home of Gilbert White the naturalist. This small thatched house has walls built from flattened stone cobbles, while the wall edges are of dressed stone.

Introduced in July 1994, Sunnyside is still currently available.

Produced: 1994–
Height: 2½ in./6½ cm
Versions: 1
Backstamp: O
Current value: £RRP ($RRP)

Sussex Mill

English Collection – South-East

Based upon a building to be found south of the Sussex Weald, Sussex Mill is a small mill with an undershot wheel. The use of clay tiles and hipped roof show its vernacular origins, and the walls would have been a mixture of soft stone, bricks and flint.

One of the early Lilliput Lane models, Sussex Mill was introduced in September 1982. However, in July 1984 it

S

Front view of version 2 (left) and version 1 (right) which has the additional windows and the cutaway base

Rear view of version 2 (left) and version 1 (right) which has the additional windows

was remodelled and the following changes made: the rear wall now had five windows (previously there had been seven); the side wall now had one window (previously there had been two); there was more foliage on the side wall and around the window; the windows in the roof were positioned higher up; the window in the roof on the left side was removed; and the base became more circular without a cutaway.

Sussex Mill was retired in March 1986.

Produced: 1982–86
Height: 2½ in./6 cm
Versions: 2
Backstamp: A, D
Current value:
   Version 1 − £500–600 ($750–1,000)
   Version 2 − £225–275 ($350–450)

Side view of version 2 (left) and version 1 (right) which has the additional windows and less foliage

The Swan Inn

English Collection – South-East

Located in Midhurst in Sussex, The Swan Inn is a 15th-century timber-framed building. Whilst some repair work was being carried out a portion of a 15th-century mural was found; it is now displayed in the Inn.

Introduced in February 1988, The Swan Inn was retired in December 1992.

Produced: 1988–92
Height: 5 in./12½ cm
Versions: 1
Backstamp: H
Current value: £90–110 ($150–175)

Sweet Briar Cottage

Classics Collection

Based upon the building in Blaise Hamlet, near Bristol, Sweet Briar Cottage is built from Cotswold stone and roofed with split stone.

Introduced in February 1993, this miniature sculpture is still current, although it is due to be retired in March 1995.

Produced: 1993–95
Height: 2-3/8 in./6 cm
Versions: 1
Backstamp: N
Current value: £RRP ($RRP)

S

Sweet Briar Cottage

English Collection – South-West

Originally designed and built around 1810 by the architects John Nash and George Repton, Sweet Briar Cottage is the smallest of the cottages in Blaise Hamlet near Bristol.

Introduced in February 1990, Sweet Briar Cottage was initially in the Blaise Hamlet Collection but in 1994 was transferred to the English Collection – South-West. The cottage is still current although it is due to be retired in March 1995.

Produced: 1990–95
Height: 4½ in./11½ cm
Versions: 1
Backstamp: K
Current value: £RRP ($RRP)

Sweet Pea Cot

English Collection – South-West

Based upon a similar cottage at Selworthy in Somerset, this stone-built thatched gate-lodge provided housing for retired workers from the Holnicote estate. Selworthy, which is renowned for its picturesque cottages, is owned by the National Trust.

Introduced in July 1994, Sweet Pea Cot is still current.

Produced: 1994–
Height: 2-3/8 in./6 cm
Versions: 1
Backstamp: O
Current value: £RRP ($RRP)

Swift Hollow

English Collection – South-East

To be found in Hampshire, this timber-framed house was built in the 17th century. Over the years some loss has occurred where panels have decayed and been replaced by brick, some of the deep thatch has been replaced by tiles and in some sections oak weatherboarding protects the timber framing.

Introduced in February 1988, Swift Hollow was retired in December 1990.

Produced: 1988–90
Height: 3¼ in./8 cm
Versions: 1
Backstamp: H
Current value: £65–75 ($80–100)

S

Tanglewood Lodge

English Collection – South-East

Tanners Cottage

English Collection – Midlands

Tanners Cottage can be found close to Bedford, in an area where many of the battles were fought in the Civil War. The cottage, which is built of Cotswold stone with a thatched roof, has its own distinctive style.

Introduced in July 1987, Tanners Cottage was retired in December 1992.

Produced: 1987–92
Height: 2 in./5 cm
Versions: 1
Backstamp: G
Current value: £20–30 ($35–45)

The eastern Cotswolds bordering the Wychwood Forest and the Evenlode Valley became a fashionable area – both as a place to visit and as a place to live – during the reign of Queen Victoria. Buildings such as Tanglewood Lodge were constructed in response to the fashion.

Introduced in February 1989, Tanglewood Lodge was retired in December 1992.

Produced: 1989–92
Height: 4½ in./11¼ cm
Versions: 1
Backstamp: J
Current value: £55–65 ($100–125)

Tea Caddy Cottage

English Collection — South-East

Tea Caddy Cottage is situated in Constable country on the Suffolk–Essex border just north of Higham. An unusual oval-shaped cottage with its Gothic-type design, the excellent brickwork is topped by a red clay tiled roof.

Introduced in February 1994, Tea Caddy Cottage is still current.

Produced: 1994–
Height: 3½ in./9 cm
Versions: 1
Backstamp: O
Current value: £RRP ($RRP)

Temple of Piety

Studley Royal Collection
(Limited Edition)

Studley Royal, near Ripon in Yorkshire, was created by John Aislabie and his son William between 1716 and 1781. The building of the Temple of Piety began in 1740, and the temple was originally dedicated to Hercules. However, William re-dedicated the Greek Doric temple soon after his father's death in 1742 as a symbol of filial piety. The interior, which was finished in 1748, was decorated by Guiseppe Cortese, a York plasterer.

Introduced in July 1994, Temple of Piety was limited to 5,000 pieces and was only available in the USA; it is anticipated that it will be generally available during 1995.

Produced: 1994–
Height: Not known
Versions: 1
Backstamp: O
Current value: £Not known ($RRP)

T

Thatcher's Rest

English Collection — South-East

The Meon Valley in south Hampshire is where houses such as Thatcher's Rest can be found. Built in the early 17th century with oak timber framing, the roof has a catslide thatch.

Introduced in September 1983, Thatcher's Rest was retired in December 1988.

Produced: 1983–88
Height: 3½ in./9 cm
Versions: 1
Backstamp: C
Current value: £150–180 ($325–400)

Thoor Ballylee

Irish Collection

William Butler Yeats, the Irish poet and dramatist, was attracted to the tower houses of Ireland, and subsequently bought a small ruined Norman tower. Yeats restored the tower and lived there for eleven years. The tower was of significance to him, and from 1919 there are references to the tower in many of his poems.

Introduced in July 1989, Thoor Ballylee was retired in July 1992.

Produced: 1989–92
Height: 4-1/8 in./10½ cm
Versions: 1

Backstamp: J
Current value: £60–80 ($150–200)

Three Feathers

English Collection — South-East

Three Feathers is the Lilliput Lane interpretation of a public house in Cambridgeshire, and is based upon the many medieval inns that exist in the area. Oak framed and with Tudor chimneys, the building is strong and solid.

Introduced in February 1986, the original version had a long white inn sign (which may possibly have been plastic). In April 1986, the sign was changed to black and was made of metal. Three Feathers was retired in December 1989.

Produced: 1986–89
Height: 4¾ in./12 cm
Versions: 2
Backstamp: F
Current value:
    Version 1 – £175–200 ($275–350)
    Version 2 – £80–100 ($150–175)

Tillers Green

English Collection — Midlands

Situated in the heart of Gloucestershire, this cottage is built from Cotswold stone and features stone window mullions and a flagged roof.

Introduced in February 1991, Tillers Green is still currently available.

Produced: 1991–
Height: 2¾ in./7 cm
Versions: 1
Backstamp: L
Current value: £RRP ($RRP)

T

Tintagel

English Collection –
South-West

Tintagel on the north coast of Cornwall is famous for its association with King Arthur. The village Post Office occupies a small 14th century manor house and is built from local granite and roofed with split stone tiles; it is now preserved by the National Trust.

Introduced in September 1984, Tintagel used the same mould as The Old Post Office (which was retired in 1986), but was painted in different colours. Tintagel was retired in December 1988.

Produced: 1984–88
Height: 2¾ in./7 cm
Versions: 1
Backstamp: D
Current value: £125–175 ($200–250)

Tired Timbers

English Collection – Midlands

Tired Timbers is situated at Preston-on-Stour in Warwickshire. Built in the 15th century, it is timber framed on a brick-built plinth and features an impressive brick chimney stack.

Introduced in July 1994, the model is still current.

Produced: 1994–
Height: 3 in./7½ cm
Versions: 1
Backstamp: O
Current value: £RRP ($RRP)

Titmouse Cottage

English Collection — South-West

In the vernacular style of Dorset, Titmouse Cottage is built of local stone with umbrella thatch.

Introduced in July 1989, Titmouse Cottage is still current.

Produced: 1989–
Height: 4 in./10 cm
Versions: 1
Backstamp: J
Current value: £RRP ($RRP)

Titwillow Cottage

English Collection — Midlands

Typical of the many 'black and white' timber-framed buildings to be found in Herefordshire, Titwillow Cottage is situated in the village of Eardisley near Hereford.

Introduced in July 1993, Titwillow Cottage is still current.

Produced: 1993–
Height: 2½ in./6½ cm
Versions: 1
Backstamp: N
Current value: £RRP ($RRP)

T

Toll House
English Collection – South-East

Typical of the cottages to be found in Hertfordshire because of its oak beams and short straw thatch, at one time this cottage would have been at the beginning of a road for which travellers had to pay a toll. Although toll roads have virtually disappeared, the toll houses can still be found.

Introduced in February 1983, Toll House was remodelled that same year when it became smaller. The versions can be distinguished by the backstamp: version 2 was only produced with backstamp C, whereas version 1 carried either backstamp A or backstamp C.

Toll House was retired in February 1987.

Produced: 1983–87
Height: 2¼ in./5½ cm
Versions: 2
Backstamp: A, C
Current value:
    Version 1 – £175–200 ($250–300)
    Version 2 – £110–140 ($150–175)

These two illustrations of version 1 (left) and version 2 (right) show the difference in size between the models

Troutbeck Farm

English Collection – Northern

Troutbeck is one of the oldest villages in the Lake District and so it has many farm buildings which date back to the 16th century. Troutbeck Farm was based on such a farm.

Introduced in September 1983, Troutbeck Farm was made from a form of terracotta; however, in 1985 the medium was changed. The noticeable differences between the two versions were that version 2 had white chimney pots and the sheep were brighter in colour. Troutbeck Farm was retired in December 1987.

Troutbeck Farm was also produced using resin, although to date only one piece is known to exist.

Produced: 1983–87
Height: 3½ in./9 cm
Versions: 3
Backstamp: C, E
Current value:
   Version 1 – £300–350 ($600–700)
   Version 2 – £175–250 ($325–400)
   Resin – £5,000+ ($8,000+)

T

Tuck Shop

English Collection – Northern

Lake Windermere has many gift shops which, although vernacular in style, were built by the Victorians at the time when travelling to the Lake District became popular. Tuck Shop was based upon these buildings.

Introduced in February 1983, Tuck Shop was remodelled during that same year. The first version, which carried either backstamp A or C, was light in colour, whereas on version 2 the timber frame, bay window and the roof were dark in colour. Also the centre panel of the bay window was increased from ten panes of glass to twenty panes.

Tuck Shop was retired in April 1986.

Produced: 1983–86
Height: 3½ in./8 cm
Versions: 2
Backstamp: A, C, D
Current value:
  Version 1 –
    Backstamp A £450–550 ($850–1,000)
    Backstamp C £300–350 ($650–725)
  Version 2 – £200–250 ($500–600)

Tudor Court

English Collection – Midlands

Based upon buildings to be seen in the ancient part of Shrewsbury, around Bear Steps, Tudor House portrays a 16th-century shopping area. Introduced in February 1986, Tudor House was retired in July 1992.

Produced: 1986–92
Height: 5½ in./13½ cm
Versions: 1
Backstamp: F
Current value: £145–175
  ($300–350)

Tudor Merchant
Welsh Collection

Located near the harbour in Tenby, this 15th-century Tudor merchant's house, which is now owned by the National Trust, is a reminder of the town's prosperous trading days.

Introduced in February 1991, the model is still current.

Produced: 1991–
Height: 4½ in./11½ cm
Versions: 1
Backstamp: L
Current value: £RRP ($RRP)

Two Hoots
English Collection – South-East

In the 16th and 17th centuries the use of bricks became more and more popular in vernacular building, spreading rapidly through areas where timber frame construction was the main building method. Such an area was Alresford in Hampshire, and Two Hoots is an example of a brick-built cottage with a thatched roof which can be found there.

Introduced in July 1994, the model is still current.

Produced: 1994–
Height: 3 in./7½ cm
Versions: 1
Backstamp: O
Current value: £RRP ($RRP)

T

Ugly House

Welsh Collection

Ty Hyl (Ugly House) can be found near Betws-y-Coed in the Conwy Valley. Built by two outlaw brothers in 1475, the house was a hideout for thieves until the early 19th century. Used by the Snowdonia National Park Society for its headquarters, the house was recently restored, upon completion of which it won a conservation award. Its name – Ugly House – comes from the huge ungainly boulders used in its walls,

Introduced in February 1991, the model is still current.

Produced: 1991–
Height: 2½ in./6½ cm
Versions: 1
Backstamp: L
Current value: £RRP ($RRP)

The Vicarage

Christmas Collection

Victoria Cottage

English Collection – Northern

The Vicarage is an essential building in the traditional village which is depicted in the Christmas Collection. Built from Cotswold stone and with a stone roof, the model is based upon a building near Littleworth in Oxfordshire.

Introduced in February 1994, The Vicarage is still current.

Produced: 1994–
Height: 2¾ in./7 cm
Versions: 1
Backstamp: O
Current value: £RRP ($RRP)

Victoria Cottage is typical of those first private houses which were built around 1880 when, because of Great Britain's dominance in world trade, new classes of society began to emerge and move away from rented accommodation.

Introduced in February 1989, Victoria Cottage was retired in December 1993.

Produced: 1989–93
Height: 3½ in./8½ cm
Versions: 1
Backstamp: J
Current value: £30–40 ($65–85)

Victoriana

American Landmarks
(Limited Edition)

Victoriana was introduced in June 1991 and was limited to 2,500 pieces. Only available in the USA, Victoriana was fully subscribed inside a year and was retired in May 1992.

Produced: 1991–92
Height: 6 in./15 cm
Versions: 1
Backstamp: L
Current value: £300–400 ($350–400)

Village School

English Collection – Northern

This model of a Victorian school situated in the Ribble Valley was introduced in July 1991 and is still currently available.

Produced: 1991–
Height: 3¼ in./8 cm
Versions: 1
Backstamp: L
Current value: £RRP ($RRP)

Vine Cottage

Classics Collection

From the miniature range of sculptures based upon buildings at Blaise Hamlet near Bristol, Vine Cottage is one of the cottages most frequently seen illustrated in calendars. Built by the architects John Nash and George Repton around 1810, Blaise Hamlet provided homes for the retired employees from the Blaise Hamlet estate.

Introduced in February 1993, Vine Cottage is still current, although it is due to be retired in March 1995.

Produced: 1993–95
Height: 2-3/8 in./6 cm
Versions: 1
Backstamp: N
Current value: £RRP ($RRP)

Vine Cottage

English Collection — South-West

Built around 1810 by the architects John Nash and George Repton as one of the cottages at Blaise Hamlet, Vine Cottage is built from stone and slate. Like Double Cottage, Vine Cottage has a gable which features a pigeon loft.

Introduced in February 1990, Vine Cottage was initially in the Blaise Hamlet Collection, but in 1994 was transferred to the English Collection — South-West. Vine Cottage is still currently available.

Produced: 1990–
Height: 4½ in./11½ cm
Versions: 1
Backstamp: K
Current value: £RRP ($RRP)

Wallace Station
American Collection – 1st Series

Introduced in October 1984, as with all of the other models in the American Collection, Wallace Station was retired in October 1985. During its production period 400 pieces were produced.

Produced: 1984–85
Height: 2½ in./6½ cm
Versions: 1
Backstamp: D
Current value: £450–550
($900–1,200)

Warwick Hall
English Collection – Northern

When it was first introduced in February 1983, Warwick Hall had its name embossed on the front of the base; however, towards the end of that year it was remodelled and the name removed. The first version carried either backstamp A or C, whereas version 2 carried backstamp D.

Warwick Hall was retired in December 1985.

Produced: 1983–85
Height: 5½ in./14 cm
Versions: 2
Backstamp: A, C, D

Current value:
Version 1 –
Backstamp A £1,500–1,800 ($3,000–3,500)
Backstamp C £950–1,200 ($2,500–2,800)
Version 2 – £650–850 ($1,800–2,200)

Watermeadows

Anniversary

Watermeadows is one of the two oldest houses in the village of Osmaston near Ashbourne in Derbyshire. The cottage, which in parts is almost 400 years old, is part of the estate of the Walker-Okeover family, and was originally two homes.

Introduced in February 1994, Watermeadows was only available in that year before being retired in December.

Produced: 1994
Height: 3¾ in./9½ cm
Versions: 1
Backstamp: O
Current value: £RRP
    ($RRP)

W

Watermill

English Collection – South-West

Built in the 17th century, this small overshot mill, which would have been found in Dorset, is attached to a cruck-framed thatched cottage. Many cottages such as this still survive today.

Introduced in July 1985, the early pieces were quite dark in colour especially around the watermill itself, and lacked any shine; later pieces were lighter and shinier. Watermill was retired in July 1993.

Produced: 1985–93
Height: 2¼ in./5¾ cm

Versions: 1
Backstamp: E
Current value:
    Version 1 – £30–35 ($60–85)
    Version 2 – £25–30 ($50–75)

Waterside Mill
English Collection – Midlands

Based upon old drawings and etchings of various Shropshire mills, Waterside Mill depicts a 17th-century undershot mill, which combines both living accommodation (which is of stone and thatch) and working area (which is of stone and slate).

Introduced in February 1994, Waterside Mill is still currently available.

Produced: 1994–
Height: 2-3/8 in./6 cm
Versions: 1
Backstamp: O
Current value: £RRP ($RRP)

Wealden House
English Collection – South-East

Typical of the houses found on the Sussex Weald, with the forward projecting jettied upper storeys at each end, Wealden House was built in the 15th century. There has been some repair work on the ground floor and the chimneys are a later addition. The wattle and daub panelling has been hung with tiles to provide added weather protection, and the hipped roof may once have been thatched.

Introduced in February 1987, Wealden House was retired in December 1990.

Produced: 1987–90

Height: 4½ in./11½ cm
Versions: 1
Backstamp: G
Current value: £110–135
($150–175)

Wedding Bells
English Collection — Northern

Situated at Upleatham in Cleveland, this tiny church (which dates from the 12th century), is believed to be the smallest in England. Built from local stone with a pantiled roof, the church measures 17¾ ft by 13 ft (5½ m by 4 m).

Introduced in July 1992, Wedding Bells is still current.

Produced: 1992–
Height: 3¼ in./8 cm
Versions: 1
Backstamp: M
Current value: £RRP ($RRP)

Wellington Lodge
English Collection — Midlands

All of the bridges on the Gloucester and Sharpness canal (which was completed in 1827) have opening spans, so it was necessary to have the bridges manned. Wellington Lodge was originally a bridgeman's cottage and would have been built in readiness for the canal being opened.

Introduced in February 1991, Wellington Lodge is still currently available.

Produced: 1991–
Height: 2½ in./6 cm
Versions: 1
Backstamp: L
Current value: £RRP ($RRP)

W

Wenlock Rise

Collectors Club

Offa's Dyke, which runs from the mouth of the River Dee in Clwyd to Chepstow in Gwent, is believed to have been built by Offa, King of Mercia, to mark the border between Mercia and Wales, and also to reduce raiding by the Welsh tribes. Today it is the setting for Wenlock Rise, a magnificent timber-framed house.

Introduced in October 1988, Wenlock Rise was only available to members of the Lilliput Lane Collectors Club for the twelve-month period to September 1989, after which it was retired. Wenlock Rise was never generally available.

Produced: 1988–89
Height: 6 in./15 cm
Versions: 1
Backstamp: H
Current value: £150–200 ($250–300)

Wheyside Cottage

English Collection – South-West

Built around the 1850s, Wheyside Cottage is situated on the border of Somerset and Devon. Using local stone and thatch, the cottage features arched Gothic leaded windows.

Introduced in February 1992, Wheyside Cottage is still current.

Produced: 1992–
Height: 2¾ in./7 cm
Versions: 1
Backstamp: M
Current value: £RRP ($RRP)

Wight Cottage

English Collection – South-East

The Isle of Wight is a very popular holiday resort, and as the many visitors tour around the island they see a number of very delightful and attractive cottages such as Wight Cottage.

Introduced in July 1989, Wight Cottage was retired in July 1994.

Produced: 1989–94
Height: 2¾ in./7 cm
Versions: 1
Backstamp: J
Current value: £20–25 ($60–65)

W

William Shakespeare's Birthplace 1989

English Collection – Midlands

Shakespeare was born in 1564 in this house in Henley Street, Stratford-upon-Avon. The house was his father's home and workshop, and in Shakespeare's lifetime it was two separate buildings. Built in the 16th century it is a typical middle-class dwelling of the period, and like many other buildings in the town dating from that time, it is half-timbered infilled with wattle and daub.

Introduced in July 1989, this new model of Shakespeare's birthplace had more foliage and garden around the house than its predecessor. The model was retired in December 1992.

Produced: 1989–92
Height: 3 in./7½ cm
Versions: 1
Backstamp: J
Current value: £55–65 ($150–180)

William Shakespeare's Birthplace

English Collection – Midlands

Stratford-upon-Avon has become one of the world's most famous tourist centres due to its association with William Shakespeare. Born in Henley Street in 1564, Shakespeare's birthplace was a 16th-century half-timbered house which also served as his father's workshop. It is now one of the best preserved Tudor houses in England.

Introduced in February 1983, the model was an almost perfect scale replica of Shakespeare's home. The original version had the wording 'Shakespeare's Cottage' embossed across the front of the base and was produced with either backstamp A or C.

In September 1983 the cottage was restyled when the wording across the front was removed; this version also carried backstamp C. Versions 1 and 2 had similar colouring, with the timbers and chimneys almost charcoal and the base a dark green.

At some point in 1984, the cottage was restyled again, with the base being more finely detailed and coloured light green, and the roof lighter in colour. This version carried backstamp D.

William Shakespeare's Birthplace was retired in July 1989.

Produced: 1983–89
Height: 3 in./7½ cm
Versions: 3
Backstamp: A, C, D
Current value:
   Version 1 – £575–675 ($1,200–1,500)
   Version 2 – £150–200 ($250–300)
   Version 3 – £75–100 ($100–125)

From left: version 1, version 2 and version 3

Winnie's Place

American Landmarks (Limited Edition)

Winnie's Place was built in 1881 in the Romantic Italianate style, and is the home of Winnie Watson Sweet, the owner of a collectables and gift shop in Indiana. Winnie is well known for her connections with the South Bend Show.

Introduced in June 1992, Winnie's Place was limited to 3,000 pieces and was only available in the USA; it was retired in June 1993.

Produced: 1992–93
Height: 6 in./15 cm
Versions: 1
Backstamp: M
Current value: £375–450 ($425–500)

W

Winter's Wonder

A Year in an English Garden

Introduced in July 1994, Winter's Wonder is one of four cottages portraying the seasonal changes. The seasonal portrayals are: spring (Spring Glory), summer (Summer Impressions), autumn (Autumn Hues) and winter (Winter's Wonder). Autumn Hues was also introduced in July 1994, with the remaining cottages being released in 1995.

Produced: 1994–
Height: 3-3/8 in./8½ cm
Versions: 1
Backstamp: O
Current value: £RRP ($RRP)

Wishing Well

Collectors Club

Wishing Well, which showed a traditional well-head, was introduced in March 1988 and was offered as a free gift to members joining the Collectors Club during the twelve months from March 1988 to February 1989, at which time it was retired. During the period that Wishing Well was being offered, membership of the Club increased to just over 12,500.

Produced: 1988–89
Height: 2½ in./6½ cm
Versions: 1
Backstamp: H
Current value: £90–120 ($135–175)

Witham Delph

English Collection – Midlands

To be found alongside a Lincolnshire dyke, Witham Delph is built from hand-made bricks and features a pantiled roof, which shows the influence of the trading with the Low Countries.

Introduced in July 1991, Witham Delph was retired in July 1994.

Produced: 1991–94
Height: 3-3/8 in./8½ cm
Versions: 1
Backstamp: L
Current value: £35–40 ($120–140)

De Wolhandelaar

Netherlands Collection

De Wolhandelaar (The Wool Merchant) shows a typical workshop which was used for turning wool from England into cloth; some of these workshops were established almost 600 years ago. The straight-sided bell gable became a particularly popular feature in the 18th century.

Introduced in February 1991, De Wolhandelaar (which is similar in appearance to De Branderij apart from the colouring) is still currently available.

Produced: 1991–
Height: 5¼ in./13½ cm
Versions: 1
Backstamp: L
Current value: £RRP ($RRP)

Woodcutters

English Collection – South-West

Situated in Devon, Woodcutters is a clay cob cottage with a thatched roof. In previous times the walls would have been painted with lime wash to provide waterproofing.

Introduced in February 1983, Woodcutters was restyled in 1984 when it was made smaller. Version 1 carried either backstamp A or C; version 2 carried backstamp C. Woodcutters was retired in February 1987.

Produced: 1983–87
Height: 2 in./5 cm
Versions: 2
Backstamp: A, C
Current value:
  Version 1 –
    Backstamp A £175–200 ($225–275)
    Backstamp C £125–150 ($175–200)
  Version 2 – £80–100 ($125–150)

W

Woodman's Retreat

Collectors Club

Situated on the edge of woodland near Faringdon in Oxfordshire, Woodman's Retreat is a small thatched cottage which was built in the 18th century. Timber framed with brick infill, the cottage reflects the cult at that time of the 'picturesque' with its varying roof heights jutting out at all angles.

Introduced in March 1994, Woodman's Retreat was only available to members of the Lilliput Lane Collectors Club during the Club year from March 1994 to February 1995, at which time the model was retired.

Produced: 1994–95
Height: 4-1/8 in./10½ cm
Versions: 1
Backstamp: O
Current value: £RRP ($RRP)

Wren Cottage

Collectors Club

Introduced in 1991, Wren Cottage was offered at a preferential price to existing Club members who enrolled a new member. The cottage was not available for general purchase through the Club, nor was it generally available.

Introduced in February 1991, the model was retired in February 1993.

Produced: 1991–93
Height: 2¼ in./5¾ cm
Versions: 1
Backstamp: L
Current value: £75–100 ($150–200)

Wycombe Toll House

Miscellaneous

The sixth Lilliput Lane Annual Fair was held at the Chiltern Open Air Museum near Amersham, in Buckinghamshire, on 3–4 September 1994. The Museum is dedicated to rescuing and re-building local buildings which would otherwise be demolished, and Wycombe Toll House was based upon a cottage in the Museum grounds.

Wycombe Toll House was only available to those members attending the two-day Fair, after which time the model was retired.

Produced: 1994
Height: 2¾ in./7 cm
Versions: 1
Backstamp: O
Current value: £55–75 ($200–300)

W

Yew Tree Farm
Collectors Club

Yew Tree Farm can be found in Cumbria and dates from the late 1600s. Built from rubble it was originally a single-roomed thatched house, but in 1737 it underwent major renovation when the upstairs was added. Adjoining the main house are barns and associated buildings, again built of rubble and roofed with Lakeland slate.

Introduced in October 1987 this was the second cottage which was only made available to current members of the Collectors Club. Yew Tree Farm was retired in September 1988.

Produced: 1987–88
Height: 3¼ in./8 cm
Versions: 1
Backstamp: G
Current value: £200–240 ($325–400)

Yuletide Inn
Christmas Special

Yuletide Inn, a timber framed and jettied building which dates from the 16th century, can be found on the Pilgrim's Way in Kent.

Introduced in September 1990, this was the third of the Christmas Specials and as with the others in the Collection was retired in February of the following year.

Produced: 1990–91
Height: 5¼ in./13 cm
Versions: 1
Backstamp: K
Current value: £120–150
    ($175–225)

Sussex Mill

From the English Collection – South-East, this was another of the early models produced by Lilliput Lane. Produced 1982–86, two versions were available; the illustrations show version 1 (left) and version 2 (right)

Victoriana

From the American Landmarks collection; produced 1991–92
the model was a limited edition of 2,500 pieces

Warwick Hall

From the English Collection – Northern, produced 1983–85

De Zijdewever

Netherlands Collection

The cluster of mulberries adorning the top of the spout gable identified the owner of De Zijdewever (The Silk Weaver); it was a fine home which would have had fine furnishings and silk wallhangings.

Introduced in February 1991, De Zijdewever (which was similar to Bloemenmarkt apart from the colouring) is still current.

Produced: 1991–
Height: 6¼ in./15½ cm
Versions: 1
Backstamp: L
Current value: £RRP ($RRP)

Land of Legend

Castles

The Sleeping Princess

The Ransomed King

The Golden Chalice

Exiled Prince

Produced: Mid-1980s–1988
Current value: £140–180 ($250–300)

Golden Chalice

Produced: Mid-1980s–1988
Current value: £100–120 ($175–200)

Ransomed King

Produced: Mid-1980s–1988
Current value: £140–180 ($250–300)

Red Knight

Produced: Mid-1980s–1988
Current value: £100–120 ($175–200)

Sleeping Princess

Produced: Mid-1980s–1988
Current value: £140–180 ($250–300)

Sorcerer's Retreat

Produced: Mid-1980s–1988
Current value: £100–120 ($175–200)

Wizard's Tower

Produced: 1988–89
Current value: £140–180 ($250–300)

Limited Edition Castles

Schloss Neuschwanstein

Produced: 1988–89
Current value: £500+ ($1,000+)
Limited edition of 1,500 pieces

Schloss Rheinjungfrau

Produced: 1988–90
Current value: £275–375 ($500–600)
Limited edition of 1,500 pieces

Schloss
Rheinjungfrau

Dealer Sign

Dennis the Dragon

Produced: 1986–87
Current value: £120–180 ($200–250)

227

Plaques and Plates

Plaques

Lower Brockhampton

Wishing Well Cottage

Cobble Combe Cottage

Coombe Cot (framed)

*Ashdown Hall
(framed)*

Plates

*Riverside Chapel plate by Ray Day, with
Riverside Chapel shown alongside*

*Wishing Well, a limited edition
plate produced in conjunction
with Franklin Mint*

*Country Church plate by Ray Day, with
Country Church shown alongside*

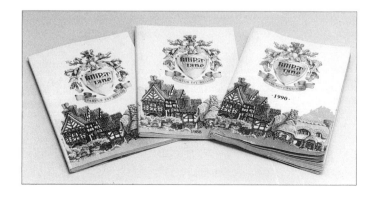

Labels

Packaging

*Early packaging,
1983–84*

*Packaging for
'Street Scene',
1986*

*Packaging,
mid-1980s*

*Packaging for
'Irish Collection'*

*Packaging,
mid-1990s*

Packaging for 'Castle Collection'

*Packaging for
'Classics Collection'*

Index